SADLIER

Vocabulary Workshop®

TOOLS FOR COMPREHENSION

Level Purple

Consultants

Joseph Czarnecki, Ph.D.
Former Faculty Associate,
School of Education
Johns Hopkins University
Baltimore, MD

Christine Gialamas
Reading Specialist
Chicago Public Schools
Chicago, IL

W9-BUA-562

Sadlier School

Reviewers

The publisher wishes to thank the following educators for their thorough review and thoughtful comments on portions of the series prior to publication.

Khawla Asmar
Principal
Salam Elementary School
Milwaukee, WI

Karen Carney
3rd Grade Teacher
Campbell City Schools
Campbell, OH

Hugh Keenan
Principal
St. Margaret of Cortona School
Bronx, NY

Carolyn Branch
Teacher/Retired Principal
Hickman Mills School District
Kansas City, MO

Cora Chlebnikow
Reading Specialist/Literacy
Consultant K–12
Madison, VA

Megan Mayfield
5th Grade Teacher
Little River Elementary School
Woodstock, GA

Susan Brody
5th Grade Teacher
South Orange Maplewood
School District
Maplewood, NJ

Scott Fillner
4th Grade Teacher
Bowman Woods School
Cedar Rapids, IA

Nancy Wahl
5th Grade Teacher
PS 41
New York, NY

Cover Series Design: Silver Linings Studios;
Cover pencil: Shutterstock.com/VikaSuh.

Photo Credits: age fotostock/Eric Baccega: 36–37 *background*. Alamy Stock Photo/David Fleetham: 28–29; Nick Hanna: 28 *top*; All Canada Photos/Chris Harris: 134 *top*; Cultura Creative/Dave & Les Jacobs: 152; Eagle Visions Photography/Craig Lovell: 85 *top*; imageBROKER: 84; iWebbstock: 76–77 *background*; KidPix: 131, 173 *top left*. Bridgeman Images/© Look and Learn/Private Collection: 143. Corbis: 100, 170 *right*; Joseph B. Strauss: 16, 169 *top left*; Ron Watts: 109, 175 *bottom left*. Dreamstime.com/Aero17: 166 *left*; Fambros: 166 *right*; Kalinn: 166 *background*; Katkov: 51; Mayangsari: 99 *top*; Mg7: 153 *top right*; Nruboc: 130; Onepony: 148 *top*. Fotolia.com/Gbuglok: 50. Getty Images/Karl Ammann: 90; Tom Brakefield: 87, 174 *top*; Ron Chapple: 30 *bottom*, 172 *top right*; Ron Dahlquist: 39; Richard During: 38, 169 *bottom left*; Jack Hollingsworth: 9; John P Kelly: 126 *inset*; Abner Kingman: 28 *bottom*; Johannes Kroemer: 36–37 *bottom*; Wayne Lynch: 76 *bottom right*; Steve Mason: 101; Ryan McVay: 60; Skip Nall: 86; Mike Powell: 98 *bottom*; Pat Powers & Cheryl Schafer: 108; Carl & Ann Purcell: 150; Alan Thornton: 20 *inset*; Jeremy Woodhouse: 20 *background*; Bettmann: 15; C Squared Studios: 31; Digital Vision: 53; Hulton Archive/Taber Photo San Francisco: 14; Photodisc: 17, 171 *center*. Gorilla Foundation/koko.org/Roy Cohn: 74. Guide Dogs for the Blind: 128 *top*, 129. The Image Works/Lebrecht Music and Arts: 142; Syracuse Newspapers/Stephen D. Cannerelli: 122. iStockphoto.com/Yenwen: 123. Library of Congress, Prints & Photographs Division/ LC-DIG-ppprs-00626: 106–107 *background*; NYWT&S Collection, LC-USZ62-111158: 64. Masterfile: 85 *bottom*, 134 *bottom*, 148 *bottom*; Minden Pictures: 145. Photodisc: 79, 175 *top left*. Photolibrary/Creatas: 144; Cultura/Zero Creatives: 126 *right*. Punchstock/National Geographic: 166 *background*. Shutterstock.com/Bigelow Illustrations: 84, 85; Elenamiv: 98–99 *background*; emo_O: 106–107 *bottom*; Graça Victoria: 153 *top left*; igorstevanovic: 106 *inset*; MustafaNC: 14 *background*; notkoo: 51 *background*; Plan-B: sunburst; SerhioGrey: 76–77; Studio 37: 98 *top*; Studio DMM Photography, Designs & Art: 99 *bottom left*; Theus: sky and clouds *background*; Triff: 76–77 *inset*; Vicente Barcelo Varona: 128–129; Gualberto Becerra: 150–151 *background*; Philip Hunton: 128 *bottom*; Eric Isselee: 77 *bottom*; JinYoung Lee: 142–143 *background*; Vladimir Melnikov: 99 *bottom left*; Mark Oleksiy: 151; Sari ONeal: 76 *bottom left*; VikaSuh: 1. Veer/Image Source Photography: 52, 171 *top*; Stockbyte Photography: 78, 171 *bottom*.

Illustration Credits: Ken Bowser: 30 *top*, 31, 33, 34, 60, 61, 63, 100, 101, 103, 104, 144, 145, 147. Mike Gordon: 58–59. CD Hullinger: 78, 79, 81, 96, 108, 109, 111, 112, 168 *left*, 172 *left*, 173 *top right*. Nathan Jarvis: 8, 9, 11, 12, 38, 39, 41, 42, 48, 122, 123, 125, 172 *bottom right*, 168 *right*, 175 *right*. Martin Lemelman: 130, 131, 133, 140, 170 *left*. Zina Saunders: 16, 17, 19, 26, 52, 53, 55, 56, 70, 86, 87, 89, 152, 153, 155, 156, 162, 169 *top right*, 169 *bottom right*, 173 *bottom right*, 174 *bottom*. Ken Spengler: 120–121. Amy Wummer: 6–7.

S® and **Vocabulary Workshop**® are registered trademarks of William H. Sadlier, Inc.

Printed in the United States of America.
ISBN: 978-1-4217-1642-8
1 2 3 4 5 6 7 8 9 BRR 23 22 21 20 19

CONTENTS

UNIT 1

Listen to this story about how a girl and her father stay safe during a thunderstorm. Pay attention to the words in the color boxes. These are the words you will be learning in this unit.

A Sudden Storm

(Realistic Fiction)

It started as a beautiful day for a hike. Nicky and her dad set out on a trail that wound through the woods behind their house. They were hiking to a farm nearby to watch the farmers care for the animals. The sun climbed higher in the sky as Nicky and her father walked. A nearby stream looked so inviting that they dipped their feet in to cool off. They got to the farm just before feeding time for the animals.

Nicky pointed at a goat. "That one is so greedy. He's eating all the feed!"

"I think it's feeding time for us, too," Dad joked. The two of them unpacked their sandwiches and sat at a picnic table to eat. After lunch, they spent some more time on the farm. Then the sun began to lower in the sky.

"We should leave before it gets too late," Dad said. "On hot sticky days like this, we often get thunderstorms by evening."

Sure enough, dark clouds were present in the sky by the time they got home. They went inside to wait for the storm to pass.

"Lightning mostly strikes taller things," Dad explained. "That's why it's wise to stay away from trees during a storm."

Outside, the wind howled and lightning lit the dark sky. A branch snapped off a tree and blew across the yard.

"I see what you mean," Nicky said.

Loud thunder sounded in the distance, and it made Nicky jump. Before long, it thundered again, but this time, she wasn't as scared.

All of a sudden, Nicky saw her dog Button dash under the couch in a blur of fur.

Dad laughed. "Button isn't quite as brave as you are."

Word Meanings

Read each word, its meaning, and the example sentence.

1. branch
(noun)
(BRANCH)

A **branch** is a part of a tree. It grows out from the trunk of the tree.

Red and yellow leaves fell from each branch of the tree.

Name some things you might see on a branch.

2. brave
(adjective)
(BRAVE)

A **brave** person is someone who is not afraid of danger.

When the cat got stuck in the tree, the brave boy climbed up to save it.

Tell about a job you have to be brave to do.

3. dash
(verb)
(DASH)

When you **dash**, you move quickly.

Don't slip if you dash across the wet grass.

Tell why someone might dash.

(noun)
(DASH)

A **dash** is a small amount of something.

The soup needs a dash of pepper.

4. evening
(noun)
(EEV-ning)

The **evening** is the part of the day between late afternoon and early nighttime.

We eat dinner in the evening after Mom comes home from work.

5. greedy
(adjective)
(GREE-dee)

A **greedy** person wants more of something than what he or she needs.

Kim was greedy when she did not share her big bowl of popcorn.

6. pass
(verb)
(PASS)

When you go by something, you **pass** it.

I pass by the park on my way home.

(noun)
(PASS)

A **pass** is a piece of paper that says the person holding it can do something.

Mom has a pass to park the car in the lot.

Permission to Park
LIC.# ATW 4137
The holder of this pass can park in the lot.

---

7. present
(noun)
(PRE-zuhnt)

A **present** is something that you give to someone out of kindness.

I drew a picture for Greg as a present.

💬 Describe a present you would like to get.

(adjective)
(PRE-zuhnt)

If you are **present** in a place, you are there.

Everyone was present on the class trip.

---

8. stream
(noun)
(STREEM)

A **stream** is a body of flowing water that is not too wide or deep.

The water in the stream only reaches my ankles.

💬 Act out something you could do at a stream.

---

9. trail
(noun)
(TRAYL)

A **trail** is a path for people to follow, especially in the woods.

I walk along the trail to the stream.

---

10. wise
(adjective)
(WIZE)

A **wise** person or choice shows good sense and judgment.

Wearing a raincoat on a wet day is a wise thing to do.

Match the Meaning

Additional activities and practice with the unit words are available at SadlierConnect.com.

Choose the word from the box that matches the meaning in the clue. Write the word on the line.

> **branch**   **dash**   **present**   **stream**   **trail**

1. You might get this on your birthday. _____

2. You might see fish swimming in this. _____

3. You might add this amount of salt to your food. _____

4. You might see birds sitting on this part of a tree. _____

5. You might find rocks as you walk along this. _____

> **brave**   **evening**   **greedy**   **pass**   **wise**

6. This is the time of the day when it starts to get dark outside.

_____

7. This is how you describe someone who does not share.

_____

8. This word describes someone who knows and understands a lot

of things. _____

9. This is how you feel when you are not scared. _____

10. This piece of paper says you can go into a building.

_____

Completing the Sentence

Choose the word from the box that best completes the sentence.
Then write the word on the line.

branch	brave	dash	evening	greedy
pass	present	stream	trail	wise

1. Grandpa gave me his old fishing pole as a _____.

2. I want to fish in the _____ right away.

3. I walk by the big, tall trees along the _____.

4. Two mice quickly _____ by my feet.

5. I feel _____ even though I hear strange sounds.

6. Oops! I bumped into a low _____ on a tree.

7. Maybe going to the stream is not a _____ idea.

8. I know I am close when I _____ the big rock.

9. I am _____ when I try to catch more fish.

10. By the time I get home, it is 6 o'clock in the _____.

Read the story. Then answer each question. Use complete sentences.

All Gone

Once upon a time, Red made a cake for Granny. She mixed some of this and some of that, a **dash** of sugar, and lots of carrots. Then she popped the cake into the oven.

Red was **brave** to walk through the woods to Granny's that **evening**. As she **passed** the **stream**, she saw a wolf.

"What's in the basket, dear?" asked the wolf.

"This cake is a **present** for Granny," Red answered.

"Come closer. I can't hear," said the wolf. Red walked closer. In a flash, the wolf gobbled up the cake.

"You ate the whole thing!" yelled Red. "You're a **greedy** wolf!"

"No, I'm a hungry wolf!" he said, **dashing** off.

1. What does the word **dash** mean in the phrase "a dash of sugar"? _____

_____

_____

2. What did Red do that was **brave**? _____

_____

_____

3. Which word in the story means "went by"? _____

_____

_____

4. Why did Red think the wolf was **greedy**? _____

_____

Write and Share

✎ *Write a story using at least three of the words in the box.*

branch	brave	dash	evening	greedy
pass	present	stream	trail	wise

_____

_____

_____

_____

_____

_____

_____

_____

_____

_____

_____

_____

💬 Talk about your work with your partner to make sure you have used the words correctly. Then write one more detail to add to your story.

_____

_____

Introducing the Words

Listen to this story about a girl who rides the first San Francisco cable car. Pay attention to the words in the color boxes. These are the words you will be learning in this unit.

The Cable Car Is Coming!

(Historical Fiction)

It was August 2, 1873, and Anna stood with her mother on Clay Street. They were not alone. A crowd of people from all over San Francisco was waiting, too. Like Anna, they wanted to ride the city's first cable car. As Anna looked at the people around her, a frown went across her face. She started to worry that she would never find a space in the cable car.

A minute later, Anna heard the bell. Clang! Clang! That was the signal that the cable car was coming! A wire cable buried deep underground pulled it up the hill. The car would cross Webster Street, then the "grip," or conductor, would turn a giant screw to bring the vehicle to a stop.

People started to move, and Anna could see the car for the first time. The car was bigger than she expected, and it was shaped like a box with flat sides. It had steps down to the ground and no wheels. The windows were open to let in fresh air. Some riders could sit on a bench along the sides or back. There were poles every few feet for other riders to hold onto as they stood.

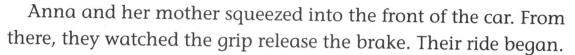
Anna and her mother squeezed into the front of the car. From there, they watched the grip release the brake. Their ride began.

In all, Anna would travel up and down Clay Street for just over a half mile and cross about ten city blocks. After the ride, Anna was so excited that she wanted more adventure. She told her mother, "Tomorrow, let's hop on a train, walk across a bridge, or ride a boat!"

Word Meanings

Read each word, its meaning, and the example sentence.

1. bench
(noun)
(BENCH)

A **bench** is a long seat for a few people to sit on.

On each side of the picnic table is a wooden bench.

💬 Describe a place where you can see a bench.

---

2. bridge
(noun)
(BRIJ)

A **bridge** is something that is built above and across water. People or cars can go over it to get to the other side.

A long bridge goes over the bay.

---

3. cross
(verb)
(KRAWSS)

When you **cross**, you go from one side to the other.

Look both ways when you cross the street.

(adjective)
(KRAWSS)

A person is **cross** if he or she is angry or not pleased.

The child was cross when the dog grabbed his toy.

💬 Show how you would look if you **were cross**.

---

4. crowd
(noun)
(KROUD)

A **crowd** is a lot of people all together in one place.

A large crowd waits for the bus.

---

5. deep
(adjective)
(DEEP)

If something is **deep**, it goes a long way down.

The children dug a deep hole in the sand.

6. fresh
(adjective)
(FRESH)

If something is **fresh**, it is clean or new.

I put on a fresh shirt for the party.

💬 **Tell about something fresh that you like.**

(adjective)
(FRESH)

Fresh means that something is cool or refreshing.

Open the windows so the fresh air can cool off the room.

7. frown
(verb)
(FROUN)

When you **frown**, you move your eyebrows together and wrinkle your forehead.

I frown when I have to go to bed early.

(noun)
(FROUN)

A **frown** is an unhappy look on your face.

When Nate found his lost puppy, his frown became a smile.

8. signal
(noun)
(SIG-nuhl)

A **signal** is an action or sign that sends a message.

The red light is a signal that means "stop."

💬 **Describe a signal a dog can make.**

9. travel
(verb)
(TRA-vuhl)

When you **travel**, you go from one place to another.

I want to travel all over the world.

💬 **Tell where you would go if you could travel anywhere.**

10. worry
(verb)
(WUR-ee)

When you **worry**, you feel that something bad may happen.

My mom and dad worry if I don't eat well.

Match the Meaning

Choose the word from the box that matches the meaning in the clue. Write the word on the line.

> **bridge   cross   deep   fresh   frown**

1. This is what you might do when you are sad. _____

2. This is how the water is when it is above your head in a pool.

_____

3. This is how you feel after a bath. _____

4. This goes over a stream so you can walk across. _____

5. This is what you are like if you are a little angry. _____

> **bench   crowd   signal   travel   worry**

6. You do this when you take a trip. _____

7. You might do this if you are lost in a crowd. _____

8. You might sit on this at the park. _____

9. You nod your head to mean "yes" as an example of this.

_____

10. You are part of this when you are with many people.

_____

Completing the Sentence

Choose the word from the box that best completes the sentence.
Then write the word on the line.

bench	bridge	cross	crowd	deep
fresh	frown	signal	travel	worry

1. Every Sunday, my mom and I _____ to the shore.

2. We like the smell of the _____ sea air.

3. To get to the other side of the bay, visitors _____ a drawbridge.

4. If a tall boat sails near the bridge, don't _____!

5. A flashing red _____ stops the traffic.

6. The boat can pass when the _____ is raised.

7. Once the bridge goes down, the _____ goes over.

8. I sit on a _____ and watch the boats.

9. Some people catch fish in the _____ waters.

10. The only time I _____ is when we have to leave.

Words in Context

Read the journal entry. Then answer each question. Use complete sentences.

Sunday, November 7

Today was the big New York City race. The runners gathered at the **bridge** that joins Staten Island and Brooklyn. They looked **fresh** and ready to go. Then the starting **signal** went off. The runners began to dash over the bridge.

Crowds stood along the streets to watch. I sat on a **bench** with my grandparents. Others watched the runners **travel** through the city from their windows.

At last I saw my brother **cross** the finish line. He was tired, but he was not **cross** about finishing last. Watching him finish the race was the best part of the day.

1. Why were the runners at the **bridge**? _____

_____

_____

2. What does "fresh and ready to go" mean? _____

_____

_____

3. What happened when the starting **signal** went off? _____

_____

_____

4. What does the phrase "not **cross** about finishing last" mean? _____

_____

_____

Write and Share

Write a story using at least three of the words in the box.

bench	bridge	cross	crowd	deep
fresh	frown	signal	travel	worry

_____

_____

_____

_____

_____

_____

_____

_____

_____

_____

_____

_____

Talk about your work with your partner to make sure you have used the words correctly. Then write one more detail to add to your story.

_____

_____

Synonyms

Circle the word that has almost the <u>same</u> meaning as the word in **dark print.** *Write the word on the line.*

1. The children **run** out of the house.
   A. pass   **B.** dash   **C.** cross   _____

2. I use pretty ribbons to wrap the **gift**.
   A. crowd   **B.** trail   **C.** present   _____

3. Birds drink water from the fresh **brook**.
   A. stream   **B.** evening   **C.** frown   _____

4. We will follow the **path** to the lake.
   A. bench   **B.** branch   **C.** trail   _____

5. Add a **bit** of oil to the pan.
   A. pass   **B.** bridge   **C.** dash   _____

Antonyms

Circle the word that has almost the <u>opposite</u> meaning as the word in **dark print.** *Write the word on the line.*

1. Jen takes a bath every **morning**.
   A. evening   **B.** bench   **C.** stream   _____

2. The king in the story was very **foolish**.
   A. greedy   **B.** brave   **C.** wise   _____

3. Put your **dirty** socks in a pile.
   A. brave   **B.** fresh   **C.** deep   _____

4. Stan has a big **smile** on his face.
   A. signal   **B.** branch   **C.** frown   _____

5. The **person** called out my name.
   A. frown   **B.** crowd   **C.** signal   _____

Classifying

Look at the words in the box. Write each word in the group in which it best fits. Use each word once.

> bench   brave   cross   deep
> fresh   greedy   trail   travel

Words That
Show Action

_____

_____

Words That Tell
About People

_____

_____

Words That Tell
About Water

_____

_____

Words That Name
Things in a Park

_____

_____

Word Associations

Choose the answer that best completes the sentence or answers the question. Pay attention to the word in **dark print**. Fill in the circle next to the answer.

1. Where would you most likely find a **branch**?
   ○ on a tree
   ○ in a crowd
   ○ under a bridge

2. What might a **brave** person do?
   ○ run and hide
   ○ talk to a friend
   ○ fight a fire

3. If you **cross** a bridge, you
   ○ travel around it.
   ○ travel over it.
   ○ travel under it.

4. In the **evening**, you eat
   ○ breakfast.
   ○ lunch.
   ○ dinner.

5. When you **worry** about something, you
   ○ think about it a lot.
   ○ joke about it.
   ○ are very brave.

6. If you use a **dash** of pepper on your taco, you use
   ○ a little bit.
   ○ a lot.
   ○ all of it.

7. Where might you see a **crowd**?
   ○ at a baseball game
   ○ on a bike
   ○ in a deep pit

8. When might you **frown**?
   ○ if you get a present
   ○ if you are lost in a crowd
   ○ if you read a good book

9. A train **pass** would let you
   ○ sit by the window.
   ○ ride on the train.
   ○ get off the train.

10. A **greedy** person does not like to
   ○ worry.
   ○ frown.
   ○ share.

Completing the Idea

Complete each sentence starter so that it makes sense.
Pay attention to the word in **dark print**.

1. On my way to school, I **pass** _____

_____

2. I would like to **travel** to _____

_____

3. To get **fresh** air, I _____

_____

4. I **frown** when _____

_____

5. Mom gets **cross** when our puppy _____

_____

6. When I see a green **signal**, I _____

_____

7. If snow is very **deep**, I _____

_____

8. A **wise** person I know said _____

_____

9. I always try to be **present** at _____

_____

10. I **cross** the bridge so I _____

_____

Word endings often do not change the meaning of a word.
The **s** or **es** ending on some words can mean "more than one."
The **ed** or **ing** ending tells when the action happens.

The ending **s** or **es** can mean that there is more than one.

crowd + s = crowds   **bench + es = benches**

The **crowds** could not all fit on the **benches**.

The ending **ed** or **ing** tells when the action happens.

dash + ed = dashed   **dash + ing = dashing**

Last night, a deer **dashed** across the yard.
A deer is **dashing** across the yard now.

Write each word without its ending.

I. presents   _____

2. traveled   _____

3. worrying   _____

4. passes   _____

Choose the word that best completes the sentence.
Write the word on the line.

5. The tree (**branches**, **bridges**) are full of leaves. _____

6. All of the (**trails**, **evenings**) lead to the stream. _____

7. A man (**frowned**, **crossed**) the road to get home. _____

8. On the way, he (**dashed, passed**) some bushes. _____

9. A girl is (**worrying**, **dashing**) to catch up to him. _____

10. They see two yellow (**signals**, **crowds**) flashing. _____

Shades of Meaning Analogies 1

Words can go together in many ways. Some words go together because they have almost the <u>same</u> meaning.

fast / quick

Think

Fast and **quick** have almost the same meaning.

Some words go together because they have <u>opposite</u> meanings.

tall / short

Think

Tall is the opposite of **short**.

Read each pair of words. Write a sentence that tells how the words go together. Tell whether the words have almost the same or opposite meanings.

1. present / gift _____

2. dirty / clean _____

3. frown / smile _____

4. trail / path _____

*Find the word in the box that has almost the same or opposite meaning as each word below. Write the word on the line. Then write **same** or **opposite** to tell how the two words go together.*

| little | morning | quiet | run | talk |

5. loud _____ _____

6. speak _____ _____

7. evening _____ _____

8. small _____ _____

UNIT 3

Listen to this article about how waves form. Pay attention to the words in the color boxes. These are the words you will be learning in this unit.

What Makes Waves?

(Magazine Article)

Imagine walking on the beach. You feel the warm sand and a seashell beneath your feet. After a while, you sit and look at the ocean. A boat on the water rises and falls. Water rolls in to the shore. It makes you wonder, "What makes waves?"

A wave is a moving ridge on the surface of a large body of water. Wind causes most waves. As wind blows over water, it gives some of its energy to the water. A small amount of wind makes a tiny wave. A strong wind can make a really big wave. Try it yourself by blowing over the top of a pan of water.

Because of the way waves seem to stack on each other, you might get the idea that the water moves forward. In fact, the water only moves up and down. You can see this motion by watching a rowboat or buoy. These objects will bob up and down with a wave, but they do not move toward or away from the shore.

When a wave near the shore breaks, the top tips over and finally crashes onto the beach.

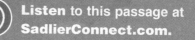
Wind is not the only thing that causes waves to form. Sometimes earthquakes and volcanic eruptions happen underwater. They can cause special kinds of very long, high waves. These giant waves rush away from the center of the action of the earthquake or volcano. You can make a model of these waves in a tub or pool. Put your arms straight out. Pull them apart and push them together again quickly. Watch how the water moves away in waves.

What makes waves? Wind, earthquakes, and volcanoes do.

Word Meanings

Read each word, its meaning, and the example sentence.

1. beach
(noun)
(BEECH)

A **beach** is land near the water. It is usually sandy.

The children looked for shells along the beach.

💬 Name some things you can see at a beach.

2. center
(noun)
(SEN-tur)

A **center** is a place that is in the middle of something.

My mom put the flowers in the center of the table.

💬 Point to the center of the room.

3. finally
(adverb)
(FYE-nuhl-ee)

Finally means "at last."

We finally finished our homework.

4. idea
(noun)
(eye-DEE-uh)

An **idea** is a thought or a plan. It is something that you think of.

Grandma had a great idea for Dad's birthday present.

5. ocean
(noun)
(OH-shuhn)

The **ocean** is a very large area of salt water. It covers almost three quarters of Earth.

Ships sail across the big, blue ocean.

💬 Use three different words to describe the ocean.

6. seashell
(noun)
(SEE-shel)

A **seashell** is the shell of a sea animal such as an oyster or a clam.

The outside of the large seashell feels rough.

7. stack
(noun)
(STAK)

A **stack** is a neat pile of something.

I ate a tall stack of pancakes.

💬 Act out putting boxes in a stack.

(verb)
(STAK)

When you **stack** things, you pile them one on top of another.

Please stack the books neatly on my desk.

8. tiny
(adjective)
(TYE-nee)

If something is **tiny**, it is very small.

A tiny drop of water dripped from the bottle.

9. wave
(verb)
(WAYV)

When you **wave**, you move your hand back and forth.

I wave to my friend.

💬 Tell some reasons why people wave.

(noun)
(WAYV)

A **wave** looks like a long bump moving through the water in a lake or an ocean.

A huge wave crashed onto the beach.

10. wonder
(verb)
(WUHN-dur)

When you **wonder** about something, you are curious about it. You want to learn about it.

I wonder why the sky is blue.

Match the Meaning

Additional activities and practice with the unit words are available at SadlierConnect.com.

Choose the word from the box that matches the meaning in the clue. Write the word on the line.

> **beach**   **idea**   **ocean**   **seashell**   **stack**

1. This is something that belongs to some sea animals.

_____

2. This is a sandy place by the water. _____

3. This is a large body of salt water. _____

4. This is a tall pile of something. _____

5. This is a plan you are thinking about. _____

> **center**   **finally**   **tiny**   **wave**   **wonder**

6. You might do this when you greet a friend. _____

7. You might stand here so all the children can see what you are doing.

_____

8. You might say this word after you finish cleaning up your room.

_____

9. You might use this word to describe an ant. _____

10. You might do this when you want to know why something is happening.

_____

Completing the Sentence

Choose the word from the box that best completes the sentence.
Then write the word on the line.

beach	center	finally	idea	ocean
seashell	stack	tiny	wave	wonder

1. I walk on the soft sand at the _____.

2. A whale is a large animal that lives in the _____.

3. I _____ how heavy a whale is.

4. Inside the shell I found lives a _____ crab.

5. There is a hole near the _____ of a clam's shell.

6. I also found a pretty _____ on the beach.

7. A _____ carries some shells in from the sea.

8. The wave almost washes away the _____ of pails.

9. _____ the children move the pails away.

10. That was a good _____!

Words in Context

**Read the story. Then answer each question.
Use complete sentences.**

A Summer Idea

Jenny loved the winter. But it was summer. She was at the **beach** watching the **waves**. Suddenly she had an **idea**.

Jenny began to gather **seashells** and sticks. Dad watched. "I **wonder** what she's doing," he said to himself.

Jenny made three different-size balls of sand and **stacked** them. She put the biggest ball on the bottom and the smallest ball on top. Then she stuck two long sticks in the middle ball, one stick on each side. She put seashells in the top ball to make the eyes, ears, and nose. Dad laughed. He **finally** figured out what Jenny was doing.

1. What does the word **waves** mean in the story? _____

_____

_____

2. What did Dad **wonder** about? _____

_____

_____

3. How did Jenny **stack** the balls of sand? _____

_____

_____

4. What was Jenny's **idea**? _____

_____

_____

Write and Share

✏ *Write a story using at least three of the words in the box.*

beach	center	finally	idea	ocean
seashell	stack	tiny	wave	wonder

_____

_____

_____

_____

_____

_____

_____

_____

_____

_____

_____

_____

💬 Talk about your work with your partner to make sure you have used the words correctly. Then write one more detail to add to your story.

_____

_____

Introducing the Words

Listen to this story about a family's trip to see the northern lights. Pay attention to the words in the color boxes. These are the words you will be learning in this unit.

A Midnight Rainbow
(Informational Fiction)

Lily and Jonah could not wait for spring break. All week, they talked about their trip. In a few days, they would arrive in Alaska to see the northern lights, a natural display of glowing colors in the night sky. Even though their parents had shown them pictures of the northern lights, Lily and Jonah still weren't sure exactly what to expect.

"How can rainbow colors appear in the dark?" Jonah asked.

"You'll just have to wait and see," Mom answered. "As long as we have good weather in Alaska, we should get a great show."

"I think this is the first time I'm not hoping for a snowstorm," Lily laughed.

"That's why we're going in March," Dad said. "It's not summer yet, so the sky still gets dark enough for us to see the northern lights. However, it won't be as cold and snowy as it would be in the winter."

That weekend, the family flew to Fairbanks, Alaska. There was some winter snow still on the ground, but skies were clear. Even in March, it felt cold to Lily and Jonah, especially at night. They wore winter coats and sipped hot chocolate as they waited and waited for the northern lights. It was almost midnight when a faint glow appeared where the land met the sky.

Slowly, the light grew and rose higher. It seemed to float right above the trees. Soon, the sky was painted with enormous swirls of green and yellow. Jonah was so amazed that he could barely speak.

"Awesome," he said in an excited whisper.

Read each word, its meaning, and the example sentence.

1. arrive
(verb)
(uh-RIVE)

When you **arrive** somewhere, you reach the place you set out for.

I arrive at school at 8 o'clock.

2. clear
(adjective)
(KLIHR)

When something is **clear**, it is not cloudy or dark.

There was not one cloud in the clear sky.

(adjective)
(KLIHR)

Clear can also mean that you can see through something easily.

We could see the rocks at the bottom of the clear lake.

💬 **Point out all the clear objects in the room.**

3. enormous
(adjective)
(ee-NOR-muhss)

Anything **enormous** is very big.

The elephant is enormous.

4. exactly
(adverb)
(ig-ZAKT-lee)

If something looks or happens **exactly** like something else, it looks or happens in the same way.

My bike looks exactly like yours.

💬 **Hold up two books. Tell if they are exactly alike.**

5. float
(verb)
(FLOHT)

When things **float**, they stay on top of water or in the air.

I let go of the balloon and watched it float above the tree.

6. midnight
(noun)
(MID-nite)

Midnight comes at 12 o'clock at night. It is called midnight because it is in the middle of the night.

I try to stay up until midnight, but I always fall asleep.

7. rainbow
(noun)
(RAYN-boh)

A **rainbow** is made of long stripes of color in the sky. If the sun shines after it rains, you often see a rainbow.

I can see orange, red, purple, blue, and other colors in a rainbow.

8. snowstorm
(noun)
(SNOH-storm)

A **snowstorm** happens when a lot of snow falls.

Over a foot of snow fell during the snowstorm.

💬 Act out how you would walk in a snowstorm.

9. weekend
(noun)
(WEEK-end)

The **weekend** is made up of the two days of the week called Saturday and Sunday.

I visit and eat lunch with my grandfather every weekend.

💬 Tell what you would like to do this weekend.

10. whisper
(verb)
(WISS-pur)

When you **whisper**, you speak in a very soft and quiet voice.

We whisper so that no one else will hear what we say.

💬 Whisper the names of two people you can see.

Match the Meaning

Additional activities and practice with the unit words are available at SadlierConnect.com.

Choose the word from the box that matches the meaning in the clue. Write the word on the line.

| clear | midnight | rainbow | snowstorm | weekend |

I. This is a time when most people are sleeping. _____

2. This is a big storm with a lot of snow. _____

3. This is what we call Saturday and Sunday.

_____

4. This is what you might see in the sky after it rains.

_____

5. This word describes a blue sky that has no clouds.

_____

| arrive | enormous | exactly | float | whisper |

6. You do this when you speak softly. _____

7. You do this when you get to a new place. _____

8. You see a ball do this on top of the water. _____

9. You might use this word to describe something that is very big.

_____

10. You might use this word to tell how alike twin sisters look.

_____

Completing the Sentence

Choose the word from the box that best completes the sentence.
Then write the word on the line.

arrive	clear	enormous	exactly	float
midnight	rainbow	snowstorm	weekend	whisper

1. I woke up at _____ and saw the snow falling.

2. Tomorrow is the beginning of the _____, and there is no school.

3. "We will play in the snow tomorrow," I _____ to my sister.

4. The snow clouds have gone, and the sky is _____.

5. My two friends finally _____ at 9 o'clock.

6. We make an _____ snowman.

7. His hat has all the colors of the _____ on it.

8. My sister makes a snowman _____ like ours!

9. Later that afternoon, dark gray clouds _____ in.

10. Maybe we will have another _____ tonight.

Words in Context

Read the speech balloon. Then answer each question. Use complete sentences.

> Hello, summer lovers! Today's weather is **clear**. It's almost **exactly** like yesterday. Around **midnight** tonight, clouds will move in. Don't worry, though. By the **weekend**, it will be clear and hot again.
>
> So beach lovers, **arrive** early at the beach for a good spot. If you feel hot, go for a swim in the cool, **clear** water. Or just lie back and think about that **enormous snowstorm** we had only three months ago.
>
> Until tomorrow, 1 am your Weatherwoman Wendy, with summer skies all around!

WENDY THE WEATHER WOMAN

1. What will the weather be like around **midnight**? _____

_____

_____

2. What will the weather be like by the **weekend**? _____

_____

_____

3. Why should people **arrive** early at the beach? _____

_____

_____

4. What does the word **clear** mean in the phrase "cool, **clear** water"? _____

_____

Write and Share

✎ *Write a story using at least three of the words in the box.*

arrive	clear	enormous	exactly	float
midnight	rainbow	snowstorm	weekend	whisper

_____

_____

_____

_____

_____

_____

_____

_____

_____

_____

💬 Talk about your work with your partner to make sure you have used the words correctly. Then write one more detail to add to your story.

_____

_____

Synonyms

*Circle the word that has almost the <u>same</u> meaning as the word in **dark print**. Write the word on the line.*

1. The boat sailed across the **sea**.
   A. ocean   **B.** beach   **C.** seashell   _____

2. I have a **plan** for a school play.
   A. wave   **B.** idea   **C.** ocean   _____

3. The **seashore** is covered with shells.
   A. rainbow   **B.** beach   **C.** snowstorm _____

4. There is jelly in the **middle** of the donut.
   A. center   **B.** idea   **C.** wave   _____

5. Please **pile** the newspapers in the corner.
   A. arrive   **B.** stack   **C.** whisper   _____

Antonyms

*Circle the word that has almost the <u>opposite</u> meaning as the word in **dark print**. Write the word on the line.*

1. I **leave** home at 8 o'clock.
   A. wonder   **B.** arrive   **C.** wave   _____

2. What a **huge** pumpkin!
   A. tiny   **B.** enormous   **C.** clear   _____

3. Don't **shout** so much!
   A. float   **B.** stack   **C.** whisper   _____

4. Will the toy boat **sink** in the pool?
   A. arrive   **B.** float   **C.** stack   _____

5. The **little** elephant sprayed water on us.
   A. clear   **B.** tiny   **C.** enormous _____

REVIEW UNITS 3–4

Classifying

Look at the words in the box. Write each word in the group in which it best fits. Use each word once.

clear	enormous	ocean	seashell
snowstorm	stack	tiny	whisper

Words That Tell About Size

_____

_____

Words About the Beach

_____

_____

Weather Words

_____

_____

Action Words

_____

_____

REVIEW UNITS 3–4

*Choose the answer that best completes the sentence or answers the question. Pay attention to the word in **dark print**. Fill in the circle next to the answer.*

1. What might you do at the **beach**?
   ○ climb a tall mountain
   ○ gather leaves
   ○ dig in the sand

2. Who might stand at the **center** of a stage?
   ○ a bird
   ○ a baby
   ○ an actor

3. When might you see a **rainbow**?
   ○ at night
   ○ after it rains
   ○ before it rains

4. On a snowy day, it's a good **idea** to
   ○ put on a hat and boots.
   ○ swim in the lake.
   ○ wear shorts.

5. If you **stack** blocks, you
   ○ hide them.
   ○ color them.
   ○ pile them.

6. When you **wonder** about something, you
   ○ don't care about it.
   ○ want to know more about it.
   ○ are scared of it.

7. You have **exactly** five cents if you have
   ○ a penny.
   ○ a nickel.
   ○ a dime.

8. What might a **wave** in the ocean do?
   ○ shake your hand
   ○ make you hot
   ○ splash water on you

9. What might you **finally** do at the end of the day?
   ○ write a story
   ○ play in the park
   ○ go to sleep

10. You might find **clear** water in
    ○ a muddy pond.
    ○ the dirt.
    ○ a swimming pool.

Completing the Idea

Complete each sentence starter so that it makes sense.
*Pay attention to the word in **dark print**.*

1. If I **arrive** late at school, I _____

_____

2. When it is dark and cloudy, I **wonder** if _____

_____

3. After the **snowstorm**, I _____

_____

4. On a sunny and **clear** day, I _____

_____

5. At the beach, the giant **wave** _____

_____

6. When I go to the **beach**, I _____

_____

7. On the **weekend**, I _____

_____

8. When I **finally** go to the park, I _____

_____

9. At **midnight**, I _____

_____

10. The bus arrived at **exactly** _____

_____

Word Study Compound Words

> A **compound word** is made up of two smaller words. Sometimes, the smaller words can help you figure out the meaning of the compound word.
>
> **mail + box = mailbox**
>
> A **mailbox** is a box for your mail.

Put the words together to make a compound word. Write the new word on the line.

1. snow + storm = _____

2. sea + shell = _____

3. rain + bow = _____

4. week + end = _____

5. mid + night = _____

*Read each sentence. Write **yes** if the sentence gives the meaning of the word in **dark print**.*

6. A **snowstorm** is a storm with lots of snow. _____

7. A **seashell** is the shell of a sea animal. _____

8. A **rainbow** is a bow made from rain. _____

9. A **weekend** is the days at the end of a week. _____

One sentence above does not give the correct meaning of the compound word. Write the correct meaning of the word below.

10. _____

_____

Shades of Meaning Word Families

A **word family** is a group of related words that share some meaning. If you know one word in a family, you have an idea about what the other words mean.

wonder	something that amazes A rainbow is a **wonder** of nature.
wonderful	very good or amazing You might say that a **wonderful** idea is a great idea.
wonderfully	in a great or wonderful way You might say that a song is **wonderfully** sung.

*Read each sentence. The words in **dark print** are related to words in the box. Circle the word that best completes the sentence.*

add   arrive   fresh   wonder

1. When I find a sum, I am doing (**arrival**, **addition**).

2. We had a (**fresher**, **wonderful**) time at the school play.

3. I opened the box as soon as it (**arrived**, **wondered**).

4. Our clothes are all (**additionally**, **freshly**) washed.

Add the ending to form a related word. Then write a sentence with the new word. The first one has been done for you.

5. sing + er = _____singer_____

The singer has a beautiful voice.

6. quiet + ly = _____

_____

7. art + ist = _____

_____

UNIT 5

Listen to this passage and recipe to learn how to make fruity pineapple pancakes. Pay attention to the words in the color boxes. These are the words you will be learning in this unit.

Pineapple Pancakes
(Recipe/How-to)

How would you like to nibble on your very own taste of the rain forest? One fruit that you know is actually grown there. It's the pineapple! This juicy fruit is popular and good for you. It can be added to a fruit salad or even cooked with meat. In some cultures, this fancy fruit has become known as a sign of welcome. On a tropical island, you may see pineapples on display in a hotel, inn, or other place that visitors go.

One simple and fun way to enjoy pineapple is to make pineapple pancakes. Here is a recipe. It will take you less than one hour to make and eat the pancakes. As any recipe will warn you, be sure to read the instructions carefully, and always cook with an adult.

Pineapple fruit is bright yellow, but the pancakes will be pale in color. You can put more pineapple on your pancakes before eating them. Be sure to chew slowly to enjoy every fruity bite!

Pineapple Pancakes

Makes eight 4-inch round pancakes

1 ¼ cup flour
3 teaspoons baking powder
1 tablespoon sugar
½ teaspoon salt

1 egg, beaten
1 cup milk
2 tablespoons oil
½ cup crushed pineapple, drained

Mix the flour, baking powder, sugar, and salt in a bowl. In another bowl, mix the egg, milk, and oil. Stir this mixture into the first mixture. The batter will be lumpy. Stir in the pineapple.

Lightly grease a griddle or pan, and heat it. Drop large spoonfuls of batter onto the griddle or pan. Turn over each pancake when the underside is golden brown. Cook until the other side is also golden brown.

Word Meanings

Read each word, its meaning, and the example sentence.

1. bright
(adjective)
(BRITE)

If something is **bright**, it gives a lot of light.

The sun is bright today.

💬 Point to something bright and tell about it.

(adjective)
(BRITE)

Something **bright** can also mean something that is shiny.

I scrubbed the pot until it looked bright and clean.

---

2. chew
(verb)
(CHOO)

When you **chew** something, you break it into small pieces with your teeth.

I chew my food before I swallow it.

💬 Name something you can chew. Then act it out.

---

3. flour
(noun)
(FLOUR)

Flour is a powder made from grain. It is used to make bread, cakes, and pies.

We put a cup of flour into the bowl with the milk and eggs.

---

4. forest
(noun)
(FOR-ist)

A **forest** is a large area that has trees and plants.

Deer live in the forest.

---

5. hour
(noun)
(OUR)

An **hour** is an amount of time. It is sixty minutes long.

It takes one hour to bake the cake.

💬 Tell what you were doing one hour ago.

6. inn
(noun)
(IN)

An **inn** is a small place where a person can eat a meal and stay for the night. It is usually in the country.

After traveling all day, we stopped at an inn for the night.

7. island
(noun)
(EYE-luhnd)

An **island** is a piece of land with water all around it.

It took the boat two hours to sail around the island.

8. nibble
(verb)
(NI-buhl)

If you **nibble** on something, you eat it with very small bites.

Rabbits nibble on carrots.

💬 **Name something you can nibble. Then act it out.**

9. pale
(adjective)
(PAYL)

If something is **pale**, it has very little color.

Jason's face looks pale because he is very sick.

10. warn
(verb)
(WORN)

If you **warn** someone, you tell the person about possible danger. A sign or signal can also warn.

The signs warn us not to walk on the ice.

💬 **Tell about something you might warn people about.**

DANGER! THIN ICE

DO NOT CROSS!

Match the Meaning

 Additional activities and practice with the unit words are available at SadlierConnect.com.

Choose the word from the box that matches the meaning in the clue. Write the word on the line.

> flour   forest   hour   island   nibble

1. This is land that has water all around it. _____

2. This is 60 minutes long. _____

3. This is a place that has many trees and plants. _____

4. This is made from grain and used in baking. _____

5. This is what you do when you take little bites. _____

> bright   chew   inn   pale   warn

6. This is a place where you can stop and sleep. _____

7. This word tells about something that has little color.

_____

8. You do this to tell someone about danger. _____

9. You might use this word to tell about something shiny.

_____

10. You do this with your teeth to break up food. _____

Completing the Sentence

Choose the word from the box that best completes the sentence.
Then write the word on the line.

bright	chew	flour	forest	hour
inn	island	nibble	pale	warn

1. The chicks sleep for an _____, and then they wake up.

2. They can see the _____ moon in the sky.

3. They find tiny specks of white _____ on the trail.

4. They begin to _____ on the tiny grains.

5. The chicks walk through the dark _____.

6. They pass by an _____ where people are sleeping.

7. Then they see an _____ in the middle of the lake.

8. They can see a garden full of corn in the _____ light.

9. Signs _____ the chicks of foxes on the island.

10. The chicks would love to _____ the corn.

Words in Context

Read the story. Then answer each question. Use complete sentences.

The Lion and the Mouse

One **bright** sunny day, Lion was asleep in the **forest**. Mouse saw a **bright** new coin on the ground. He rushed to grab it and ran right over Lion's nose!

Lion grabbed Mouse and roared, "I **warn** you. Don't ever do that again!"

"I won't," said Mouse. "Let me go, and one day I'll save your life."

Lion laughed but let Mouse go. An **hour** later, hunters caught Lion in a net. Mouse heard Lion's cries.

He ran over and said, "I will **nibble** on the net."

"Don't nibble!" Lion said. "**Chew** fast!"

And that was just what Mouse did. From then on, Lion and Mouse were great friends.

1. What does the word **bright** mean in the phrase "**bright** new coin"?

_____

_____

2. What does Lion **warn** Mouse about? _____

_____

3. What happens an **hour** after Mouse leaves Lion? _____

_____

_____

4. Why does Lion want Mouse to **chew** rather than **nibble** on the net?

_____

_____

Write and Share

✎ *Write a story using at least three of the words in the box.*

bright	chew	flour	forest	hour
inn	island	nibble	pale	warn

_____

_____

_____

_____

_____

_____

_____

_____

_____

_____

_____

💬 Talk about your work with your partner to make sure you have used the words correctly. Then write one more detail to add to your story.

_____

_____

UNIT 6

Introducing the Words

Listen to this folktale about why bears have short tails. Pay attention to the words in the color boxes. These are the words you will be learning in this unit.

Why Bears Have Short Tails

(Folktale)

Many years ago, Bear had a long, fluffy tail. Every morning, she would boast, "I think my tail looks so very pretty today."

The other forest animals were too weak to stand up to her. Instead, they could only agree.

"It's a nice tail," Rabbit and Chipmunk would say in gentle voices.

Then one cold, winter day, Fox had a clever idea. He was famous for being tricky. Fox asked all the animals to help him catch lots of fish. Then he found a spot where he could sit on the frozen pond and put all the fish around him. He knew Bear would come by to search for food.

Fox sat on the ice and waited. Up above, the bare winter branches blew in the brisk wind. At last, Bear arrived. She licked her lips and came over to Fox.

"How did you catch so many fish?" Bear asked.

"I used my tail," Fox said. "I bet you'd catch even more with your lovely tail. Try it here. This is the best spot for fishing."

Bear made a hole in the icy pond and dipped her tail in the dark, cold water.

Fox rubbed his paws together. "Tonight, we'll have a fish feast."

"We?" chuckled Bear. "You mean *I'll* have a fish feast tonight."

Fox shrugged. "Whatever you say. You're the leader of this forest."

Bear sat on the ice for a long time. She sat so long that she fell asleep. When she woke hours later, she didn't notice that her tail had frozen into the ice. She tugged hard at her tail, and part of it snapped off!

"My beautiful tail!" Bear cried, running off in shame.

From then on, Fox was a hero in the forest. The forest animals didn't have to hear about Bear's tail ever again.

Word Meanings

Read each word, its meaning, and the example sentence.

1. agree
(verb)
(uh-GREE)

When you **agree** with someone, you think the same way as the other person.

Sam and I agree that ice skating is fun.

💬 Move your head to show you agree with what someone said or did.

2. bare
(adjective)
(BAIR)

If something is **bare**, it is not covered.

I put my bare legs into the water.

3. famous
(adjective)
(FAY-muhss)

A **famous** person is someone who is known by many people.

Babe Ruth is a baseball player who is famous.

💬 Describe a famous person you have read about.

4. feast
(noun)
(FEEST)

A **feast** is a very large meal on a special day.

Mom cooks a feast on Thanksgiving Day.

5. gentle
(adjective)
(JEN-tuhl)

If something is **gentle**, it is very soft and mild.

I gave my baby sister a warm and gentle hug.

💬 Act out how you would be gentle with a small pet.

6. hero
(noun)
(HIHR-oh)

A **hero** is a person you look up to for having done something good and brave.

The boy is a hero for rescuing the cat from the tree.

7. leader
(noun)
(LEE-dur)

A **leader** is a person who shows people where to go or how to do something.

We followed the leader up the path.

8. notice
(verb)
(NOH-tiss)

If you **notice** something, you see it.

The mouse was so quiet that the cat did not notice it.

💬 Look at the floor and tell what you notice.

(noun)
(NOH-tiss)

A **notice** is a sign put up for people to read.

Dad read the notice about the missing dog.

9. search
(verb)
(SURCH)

If you **search** for something, you look for it.

Please help me search for my lost shoes.

💬 Show how you search for something in your pockets.

10. weak
(adjective)
(WEEK)

If you feel **weak**, you do not feel strong.

You cannot lift that heavy box if you are weak.

Match the Meaning

 Additional activities and practice with the unit words are available at SadlierConnect.com.

Choose the word from the box that matches the meaning in the clue. Write the word on the line.

agree	feast	hero	notice	search

1. You do this when you see something. _____

2. You do this when you look for something. _____

3. You do this when you and another person think alike.

_____

4. This is a person who is brave and good. _____

5. This is a huge meal that celebrates a special day.

_____

bare	famous	gentle	leader	weak

6. This is how you describe a person who many people know.

_____

7. This is a person who is in charge. _____

8. This is how you describe a person who is soft and mild.

_____

9. This word describes a person who is not strong. _____

10. This word describes something that is not covered.

_____

Completing the Sentence

Choose the word from the box that best completes the sentence.
Then write the word on the line.

agree	bare	famous	feast	gentle
hero	leader	notice	search	weak

1. The town put up a _____ about the big party.

2. Everyone will enjoy a delicious _____ tomorrow.

3. We are honoring a girl who became a _____.

4. She saved a puppy that was too _____ to swim.

5. A reporter wrote a story about the girl and made her

   _____.

6. The musicians marched behind the band _____.

7. My _____ arms got burned from too much sun.

8. I had to _____ for my mother in the crowd.

9. Mom was _____ as she put lotion on my skin.

10. This is the best party ever! Don't you _____?

Read the biography about Dr. Martin Luther King, Jr.
Then answer each question. Use complete sentences.

Dr. Martin Luther King, Jr.

Dr. Martin Luther King, Jr., was a great **leader**. People **noticed** him wherever he went. He helped all people, both the **weak** and the strong. He was a kind and **gentle** man.

People looked for **notices** telling of Dr. King's events. They wanted to join his peaceful marches. And they wanted to hear his exciting speeches. Dr. King's most **famous** speech is called "I Have a Dream." He dreamed that one day all Americans would be free. They would live together in peace.

Dr. King was born on January 15, 1929. He died in 1968. Today, people **agree** that Dr. King is a **hero**. In 1983, his birthday became a national holiday.

1. Why was Dr. Martin Luther King, Jr., a great **leader**? _____

_____

_____

2. What did people learn about Dr. King's events from the **notices**? _____

_____

_____

3. Why do you think the speech "I Have a Dream" is so **famous**? _____

_____

_____

4. Why is Dr. King a **hero** to many people? _____

_____

_____

Write and Share

✎ *Write a story using at least three of the words in the box.*

agree	bare	famous	feast	gentle
hero	leader	notice	search	weak

_____

_____

_____

_____

_____

_____

_____

_____

_____

_____

💬 Talk about your work with your partner to make sure you have used the words correctly. Then write one more detail to add to your story.

_____

_____

Synonyms

Circle the word that has almost the same meaning as the word in **dark print.** Write the word on the line.

1. The star of the show is **well-known**.
   A. weak   B. bright   C. famous   _____

2. We did not **see** that my brother was behind us.
   A. notice   B. search   C. warn   _____

3. We **look** for acorns in the forest.
   A. chew   B. search   C. warn   _____

4. The new coin is silver and **shiny**.
   A. pale   B. bright   C. famous   _____

5. The rabbit ran into the **woods**.
   A. hero   B. island   C. forest   _____

Antonyms

Circle the word that has almost the opposite meaning as the word in **dark print.** Write the word on the line.

1. The boy runs on **strong** legs.
   A. weak   B. famous   C. bare   _____

2. My brother and I **fight** about everything.
   A. chew   B. search   C. agree   _____

3. I cannot read in the **dim** light.
   A. bare   B. bright   C. pale   _____

4. The **wild** animal licked its pup.
   A. weak   B. gentle   C. pale   _____

5. We had a **snack** after the show.
   A. inn   B. island   C. feast   _____

Classifying

Look at the words in the box. Write each word in the group in which it best fits. Use each word once.

| chew | hero | inn | island |
| leader | nibble | search | warn |

Words That Tell About Eating

_____

_____

Words That Name Places

_____

_____

Words About a Special Person

_____

_____

Words That Show Action

_____

_____

Word Associations

*Choose the answer that best completes the sentence or answers the question. Pay attention to the word in **dark print**. Fill in the circle next to the answer.*

1. What things can you make with **flour**?
   - ○ trees
   - ○ cupcakes
   - ○ pictures

2. What can you do for one **hour**?
   - ○ hold my breath
   - ○ jump rope
   - ○ play at the park

3. Try to be **gentle** when you
   - ○ hold a nail and hammer.
   - ○ eat lunch.
   - ○ touch a baby.

4. When can the moon be very **bright**?
   - ○ at midnight
   - ○ at noon
   - ○ in the morning

5. What kinds of food would a rabbit **nibble**?
   - ○ fish, honey, bugs
   - ○ carrots, lettuce, celery
   - ○ soup, rice, meat

6. What would you most likely ride on to get to an **island**?
   - ○ a train
   - ○ a boat
   - ○ a bike

7. You might **warn** someone about
   - ○ walking on an icy lake.
   - ○ taking a nap.
   - ○ finding a pencil.

8. What colors are **pale**?
   - ○ red, purple, orange
   - ○ pink, gray, light blue
   - ○ yellow, black, green

9. You might walk with **bare** feet when you are
   - ○ in the forest.
   - ○ at an inn.
   - ○ at the beach.

10. You might put up a **notice** to tell people that
    - ○ your cat is lost.
    - ○ your telephone is ringing.
    - ○ you swept the floor.

Completing the Idea

Complete each sentence starter so that it makes sense.
*Pay attention to the word in **dark print**.*

1. I **agree** with my friend when she says _____

_____

2. George Washington is **famous** because _____

_____

3. My favorite foods at a **feast** are _____

_____

4. I am **gentle** when I _____

_____

5. My favorite **hero** is _____

_____

6. Every day, I **notice** that _____

_____

7. I **chew** my food well because _____

_____

8. When I go to the **forest**, I see _____

_____

9. I am a **leader** when I _____

_____

10. Every morning, I **search** for _____

_____

Word Study — Homophones

A **homophone** is a word that sounds just like another word but has a different meaning and spelling.

Flower and **flour** are homophones.

The rose is my favorite **flower**.
I need a cup of **flour** to make the pie crust.

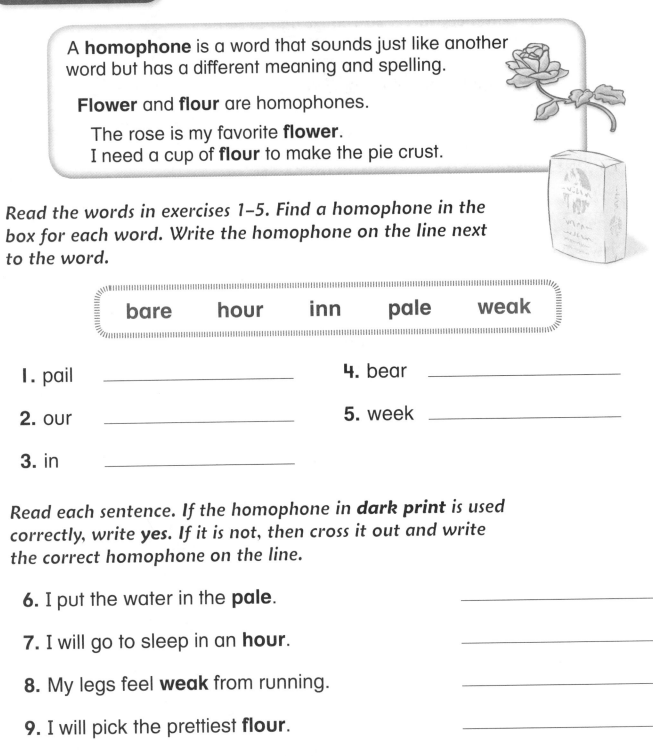

Read the words in exercises 1–5. Find a homophone in the box for each word. Write the homophone on the line next to the word.

| bare | hour | inn | pale | weak |

1. pail _____

2. our _____

3. in _____

4. bear _____

5. week _____

Read each sentence. If the homophone in **dark print** is used correctly, write **yes.** If it is not, then cross it out and write the correct homophone on the line.

6. I put the water in the **pale**. _____

7. I will go to sleep in an **hour**. _____

8. My legs feel **weak** from running. _____

9. I will pick the prettiest **flour**. _____

10. The **bare** ate honey from the tree. _____

Shades of Meaning   Word Choice 1

You learned the meaning of the word **search** on page 61.
Look at the chart for words that are close in meaning to
search. Notice how the meanings of the words are alike
and different.

look	When you **look** at something, you use your eyes to see it. You use your eyes to **look** at a picture.
search	When you **search** for something, you look long and hard for it. Something you **search** for might be hard to find.
watch	When you **watch** something, you look at it for quite some time. It might take an hour to **watch** a movie.

Write the word from the chart that best completes each sentence.

1. When my dog ran away, I went to _____ for it.

2. I like to _____ my brother dance.

3. We had to _____ through the closet for my hat.

4. I like to _____ out the window when I'm in the car.

5. It's fun to _____ at pictures of faraway places.

6. We woke up early to _____ the sunrise.

*In each exercise, circle the word in **dark print** to answer the
first question. Then answer the second question. Use the word
you chose in your answer.*

7. Would you **search** or **watch** someone do a trick? Why?

_____

8. Would you **watch** or **search** for a lost shoe? Why?

_____

Match the Meaning

Choose the word that best matches the meaning.
Fill in the circle next to the word.

1. a path
- ○ forest
- ○ feast
- ○ trail
- ○ flour

2. the middle
- ○ center
- ○ rainbow
- ○ branch
- ○ stack

3. to take a trip
- ○ dash
- ○ search
- ○ float
- ○ travel

4. far down
- ○ bright
- ○ bare
- ○ enormous
- ○ deep

5. to go by
- ○ arrive
- ○ pass
- ○ cross
- ○ stack

6. a small body of water
- ○ ocean
- ○ stream
- ○ beach
- ○ bridge

7. something to sit on
- ○ evening
- ○ leader
- ○ bench
- ○ seashell

8. something you can cross by car
- ○ wave
- ○ ocean
- ○ bridge
- ○ hour

9. where you find sand and seashells
- ○ beach
- ○ stream
- ○ inn
- ○ snowstorm

10. easy to see through
- ○ tiny
- ○ brave
- ○ fresh
- ○ clear

Completing the Sentence

Choose the word that best completes the sentence.
Fill in the circle next to the word.

11. On Sunday, I can _____ sleep late.
    ○ clear   ○ finally   ○ exactly   ○ center

12. We plan to _____ at the movie on time.
    ○ float   ○ warn   ○ cross   ○ arrive

13. A large _____ waits on the ticket line.
    ○ seashell   ○ rainbow   ○ crowd   ○ island

14. There aren't many seats left, so I start to _____.
    ○ worry   ○ pass   ○ chew   ○ nibble

15. After eating all of the popcorn by myself, I feel _____.
    ○ tiny   ○ greedy   ○ pale   ○ brave

16. During the movie, I must _____ when I talk.
    ○ whisper   ○ frown   ○ wave   ○ signal

17. "Is it fun to be an actor?" I _____.
    ○ frown   ○ worry   ○ travel   ○ wonder

18. The knight who fights a dragon is _____.
    ○ fresh   ○ brave   ○ wise   ○ deep

19. Seeing two movies in one day is a great _____!
    ○ bench   ○ signal   ○ idea   ○ crowd

20. I will go to the movies again next _____.
    ○ weekend   ○ hero   ○ midnight   ○ snowstorm

Read this passage about an amazing gorilla. Then answer the questions.

Koko and Penny Patterson with a pet cat

Koko the Gorilla

Koko was a **famous** gorilla. She used her hands to make signs for words. In this way, she "talked" to people.

Koko was born in a zoo. When she was a baby, she became **weak** and sickly. After special care, Koko became healthy. Soon she met Penny Patterson. Penny became her teacher. She started teaching Koko simple signs for words like *eat* and *drink*. Koko knew over one thousand signs.

When Koko was fifteen years old, Penny gave her a **present**. Penny let Koko choose a pet. Koko picked out a **tiny** gray kitten that had no tail. She named him "Smoky." Koko was **gentle** with Smoky. She treated him like a baby. She did not get **cross** with him.

No one is sure exactly how much Koko knew, but most people can **agree** that Koko was one smart gorilla.

Choose the answer that best completes the sentence or answers the question. Fill in the circle next to the answer.

21. The word **famous** means
- ○ sad.
- ○ well known.
- ○ very tired.

22. What does the word **weak** mean?
- ○ not warm
- ○ heavy
- ○ not strong

23. In this passage, the word **present** means
- ○ here.
- ○ show.
- ○ gift.

24. What phrase helps you know the meaning of **present**?
- ○ "Koko was a famous gorilla"
- ○ "Koko picked out a tiny gray kitten"
- ○ "Koko was gentle with Smoky"

25. What does the word **tiny** mean?
- ○ very large
- ○ very small
- ○ striped

26. What does the word **gentle** mean?
- ○ soft and mild
- ○ angry and loud
- ○ shy and scared

27. In this passage, the word **cross** means
- ○ sad.
- ○ clean.
- ○ angry.

28. When people **agree**, they
- ○ think the same way.
- ○ get into a fight.
- ○ do not like each other.

29. What would make another good title for this passage?
- ○ "Smoky the Kitten"
- ○ "A Gorilla That Can Sign"
- ○ "All About Gorillas"

30. The author most likely wrote this passage to
- ○ tell a story about a kitten.
- ○ give facts about a real gorilla.
- ○ teach people sign language.

UNIT 7

Listen to this article about the amazing world of insects. Pay attention to the words in the color boxes. These are the words you will be learning in this unit.

Be an Outdoor Detective

(Magazine Article)

In the animal world around us, there are lots of small creatures waiting for you to discover. Many of these critters belong to the insect family. All insects have three main body parts and six legs. However, insects come in all shapes, sizes, and colors. They can be found anywhere from a dry desert to a damp swamp.

Some insects are so small that you may need a tool such as a hand lens to see them. Other insects have features that make

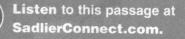
them easy to find. For example, you can easily see a colorful butterfly on a plant. And, you will know it when a bee is buzzing like an alarm near your ear.

Many insects are quite busy at work. When butterflies and bees land on flowers, their bodies often pick up a powder called pollen. Then when they fly to other flowers, they scatter the pollen. This helps create more plants.

Sometimes, insects work as a team. Ants are a good example. Ants work in groups called colonies. A single colony may have hundreds or even thousands of ants in it. Together, the ants work to build anthills and tunnels in soil or sand. These places give the ants a place to stay safe. Ants also work together to collect pieces of plants or food crumbs that people leave behind. Then the ants carry this food back to the anthill. Ants can even carry pieces of food that are bigger than their bodies!

Are you ready to start exploring? Pay attention to where you step, and look closely at leaves and dirt. You may see some interesting insects.

Word Meanings

Read each word, its meaning, and the example sentence.

1. alarm
(noun)
(uh-LARM)

An **alarm** is something that wakes people or warns them of danger. It could be a bell or a buzzer.

When the kitchen got smoky, an alarm sounded.

2. collect
(verb)
(kuh-LEKT)

When you gather things together, you **collect** them.

I like to collect seashells at the shore.

💬 Tell some ideas for objects to collect.

3. damp
(adjective)
(DAMP)

When something is **damp**, it is a little wet or moist.

My shoes got wet in the rain and are still damp.

4. insect
(noun)
(IN-sekt)

An **insect** is a small animal with three main body parts, six legs, wings, and no backbone. Bees, flies, and moths are **insects**.

A dragonfly is an insect found near fresh water.

5. plant
(noun)
(PLANT)

A **plant** is a living thing that grows in soil or in water. It often has green leaves.

A tree is a kind of plant.

💬 Describe a plant you have seen indoors or outdoors.

(verb)
(PLANT)

You **plant** when you put something such as a seed into the ground so it can grow.

When is the best time to plant tulips?

6. safe
(adjective)
(SAYF)

If something is **safe**, it is not in danger of being harmed or stolen.

Always put on a seatbelt to be safe in a car.

💬 Tell about a person who helps keep us safe.

(noun)
(SAYF)

A **safe** is a strong box in which you can lock up money and other valuable things.

Holly keeps her special rings in a safe.

7. scatter
(verb)
(SKA-tur)

When you **scatter** things, you throw them over a large area.

The children like to scatter bread crumbs in the pond for the ducks.

💬 Show how you would scatter a handful of seeds.

8. soil
(noun)
(SOYL)

Soil is the dirt or earth that plants grow in.

Plants need light, water, air, and soil to grow.

9. team
(noun)
(TEEM)

A **team** is a group of people who work together or play a sport together.

There are eleven players on a soccer team.

💬 Tell about a **team** you like to watch.

10. tool
(noun)
(TOOL)

A **tool** is a piece of equipment used to do a certain job.

A hammer is a tool we use to pound nails.

Match the Meaning

Additional activities and practice with the unit words are available at SadlierConnect.com.

Choose the word from the box that matches the meaning in the clue. Write the word on the line.

> alarm   collect   damp   plant   scatter

1. You do this when you put seeds into the ground. _____

2. You do this when you save stamps or coins. _____

3. You feel this way when you are in a light rain. _____

4. You hear this during a fire drill. _____

5. You do this to leaves when you throw them in the air.

_____

> insect   safe   soil   team   tool

6. This is often needed to fix something. _____

7. This is a place to keep money. _____

8. This is the dirt a plant grows in. _____

9. This group of people works together. _____

10. This small creature has wings and six legs. _____

Completing the Sentence

Choose the word from the box that best completes the sentence.
Then write the word on the line.

alarm	collect	damp	insect	plant
safe	scatter	soil	team	tool

1. Jess wakes up as soon as the _____ goes off.

2. Today her softball _____ has a big job to do!

3. First, the children _____ things for gardening.

4. Then they search the ground for fresh _____.

5. They use a _____ for digging deep.

6. After that, they _____ seeds.

7. Finally, the children water the soil so it is _____.

8. They want to keep out any bird or _____.

9. They worry that the seeds will not be _____.

10. Soon each seed will grow into a _____!

Words in Context

Read the directions on the card. Then answer each question. Use complete sentences.

How to Grow an Avocado Plant

Here's a **plant** that is easy to grow. You don't even need **soil** or a **tool** to dig with!

a. First **collect** the following things:
   • an avocado pit • a jar • four toothpicks • water
b. Stick in the toothpicks around the center of the pit. To be **safe**, don't touch the sharp ends of the toothpicks.
c. Fill the jar part-way with water.
d. Place the bigger end of the pit in the water. The toothpicks will rest on the top of the jar.
e. Finally, place the jar in a bright window.

Don't forget to clean up with a **damp** cloth!

1. What is the meaning of **plant** in the directions on the card? _____

_____

_____

2. What things do you have to **collect** to grow an avocado plant? _____

_____

_____

3. What can happen if you don't use toothpicks in a **safe** way? _____

_____

_____

4. Which word on the card means "moist" or "a little wet"? _____

_____

_____

Write and Share

✎ *Write a story using at least five of the words in the box.*

alarm	collect	damp	insect	plant
safe	scatter	soil	team	tool

_____

_____

_____

_____

_____

_____

_____

_____

_____

_____

_____

💬 Talk about your work with your partner to make sure you have used the words correctly. Then write one more detail to add to your story.

_____

_____

UNIT 8

Introducing the Words

Listen to this article about beautiful Yellowstone National Park. Pay attention to the words in the color boxes. These are the words you will be learning in this unit.

Yellowstone National Park

(Magazine Article)

Yellowstone National Park is our country's first national park. It is a large park. Parts of it are in three states: Wyoming, Montana, and Idaho. The park is famous for its natural wonders, such as waterfalls, hot springs, and geysers.

There are many reasons to visit Yellowstone National Park. One is to see the many geysers. A geyser is a natural hot spring that sprays steam and hot water into the air. The most famous geyser is Old Faithful. It can prove to you that it deserves its name. About every ninety minutes, Old Faithful blasts a steady stream of boiling water high into the sky.

A geyser sprays steam and hot water into the air.

Another reason to visit the park is to see hot springs and thick mud pots. The mud pots are pools of hot muddy water. Don't dive in though! Some are as hot as boiling water.

(( )) **Listen** to this passage at
SadlierConnect.com.

Yellowstone is home to many animals. You may be able to get a close look at a herd of wild bison, sometimes called buffalo, from your car. Many years ago, hunters were an enemy of the bison. Now the bison in the park are protected. Elk, moose, bears, and wolves are among the other animals that live in

A bison mother and calf graze in the park.

Yellowstone. Eagles, too, soar through its skies. Visitors should remember not to bother, feed, or frighten the animals in the park.

People can walk on the park's many miles of smooth walking trails. People can also camp, boat, and horseback ride. Visitors should pack a map, water, and camera. It is a good idea to seal the camera in a plastic bag to protect it from water.

Yellowstone has many amazing things to see. No wonder over sixty million people have visited this special place!

Word Meanings

Read each word, its meaning, and the example sentence.

1. dive
(verb)
(DIVE)

When you **dive**, you go head first into water with your arms stretched out in front of you.

Rick knows how to dive into the deep end of the pool.

2. enemy
(noun)
(E-nuh-mee)

An **enemy** is a person or animal that doesn't like, or wants to harm, another person or animal.

A hunter is an animal's enemy.

3. frighten
(verb)
(FRYE-tuhn)

When you **frighten** someone, you scare the person.

Yoko can frighten her brother by wearing a scary mask.

💬 Describe how you feel when something frightens you.

4. herd
(noun)
(HURD)

A **herd** is a group of animals. The herd may feed or travel together.

A herd of cattle wanders in the meadow.

5. pack
(verb)
(PAK)

When you **pack**, you put things into a container, such as a bag, box, or suitcase.

I will pack my books for school.

💬 Act out how you pack your suitcase or your backpack.

(noun)
(PAK)

A **pack** is a group of something, such as animals, people, or things.

There are six crayons in a pack.

6. prove
(verb)
(PROOV)

When you **prove** something, you show that it is true.

The experiment will prove that plants need sun to grow.

💬 Tell about a time you had to prove something.

---

7. seal
(noun)
(SEEL)

A **seal** is a sea animal that has thick fur and flippers. It can swim and live in cold places.

The seal uses its flippers to pull itself along the ground.

(verb)
(SEEL)

When you **seal** something, you close it up tightly.

Use tape to seal the box before you mail it.

---

8. smooth
(adjective)
(SMOOTH)

If something is **smooth**, it is flat and even, not rough and bumpy.

A baby's skin is soft and smooth.

💬 Point to smooth objects that are nearby.

---

9. soar
(verb)
(SOR)

To **soar** is to fly very high in the air.

Watch the bald eagle soar in the sky.

💬 Describe two things you have seen soar.

---

10. steady
(adjective)
(STE-dee)

If something is **steady**, it continues and does not change much.

We played inside all day because of the steady rainfall.

Match the Meaning

Additional activities and practice with the unit words are available at SadlierConnect.com.

Choose the word from the box that matches the meaning in the clue. Write the word on the line.

| dive | frighten | pack | prove | seal |

1. You might use a pool to do this. _____

2. You use tape or glue to do this to a box. _____

3. You do this to convince someone that something is true.

_____

4. You do this when you scare someone. _____

5. You do this when you put clothes in a suitcase. _____

| enemy | herd | smooth | soar | steady |

6. This is what a plane can do. _____

7. This is a group of horses. _____

8. This is what a spider is to a fly. _____

9. This is how a frozen lake looks. _____

10. A tightrope walker needs to be sure he feels this when he works.

_____

Completing the Sentence

Choose the word from the box that best completes the sentence.
Then write the word on the line.

dive	enemy	frighten	herd	pack
prove	seal	smooth	soar	steady

1. Jack is ready to _____ his book bag for school.

2. He wants to _____ to his mom that he knows a lot about animals.

3. One animal that swims in the ocean is a _____.

4. A penguin has a _____ black and white body.

5. Dolphins jump and _____ into the sea.

6. Zebras live in a _____ to stay safe.

7. A turtle's shell keeps it safe from its _____.

8. A bear may climb a tree when people _____ it.

9. Mom wonders how a lion is _____ on a tree limb.

10. Jack wonders what it is like to _____ like a bird.

➥ *Read the article about elephants. Then answer each question. Use complete sentences.*

Enormous Elephants

The elephant is the biggest living land animal. Males have **smooth** tusks on their faces. All elephants have three eyelids on each eye. A clear eyelid helps **seal** the eye to keep dust off it. Twenty to forty elephants live in a herd. During the day, the **herd** stands in the shade and sleeps.

In the evening, elephants look for food. They walk slowly so the young and old can keep up. At a stream they drink and wash. They swim in deep water but can't jump or **dive**.

Other animals don't **frighten** elephants, not even a **pack** of wild dogs. People are their only **enemy**.

1. How does an elephant's clear eyelid **seal** its eye? _____

_____

_____

2. How would you describe a **herd** of elephants? _____

_____

_____

3. What two words in the article are other words for "group"? _____

_____

_____

4. Why do you think other animals don't **frighten** elephants? _____

_____

_____

Write and Share

Write a story using at least five of the words in the box.

dive	enemy	frighten	herd	pack
prove	seal	smooth	soar	steady

_____

_____

_____

_____

_____

_____

_____

_____

_____

_____

_____

Talk about your work with your partner to make sure you have used the words correctly. Then write one more detail to add to your story.

_____

_____

Synonyms

Circle the word that has almost the <u>same</u> meaning as the word in **dark print**. Write the word on the line.

1. A beetle is a kind of **bug**.
   A. plant   **B.** tool   **C.** insect   _____

2. A loud noise might **scare** you.
   A. frighten   **B.** scatter   **C.** soar   _____

3. A **group** of lions will frighten the deer.
   A. seal   **B.** pack   **C.** enemy   _____

4. How can you **show** that this statement is true?
   A. pack   **B.** scatter   **C.** prove   _____

5. We heard the **even** beat of the drum.
   A. safe   **B.** steady   **C.** damp   _____

Antonyms

Circle the word that has almost the <u>opposite</u> meaning as the word in **dark print**. Write the word on the line.

1. Can you help me **open** the box?
   A. plant   **B.** seal   **C.** collect   _____

2. Please **collect** the birdseed in the cage.
   A. soar   **B.** plant   **C.** scatter   _____

3. An ant's **friend** may be another ant.
   A. alarm   **B.** enemy   **C.** team   _____

4. The boy skated across the **bumpy** ice.
   A. safe   **B.** damp   **C.** smooth   _____

5. The sand of the beach was **dry**.
   A. damp   **B.** safe   **C.** steady   _____

Classifying

Look at the words in the box. Write each word in the group in which it best fits. Use each word once.

dive	herd	insect	plant
seal	soar	soil	team

Words That Name Groups

_____

_____

Words That Name Creatures

_____

_____

Garden Words

_____

_____

Action Words

_____

_____

*Choose the answer that best completes the sentence or answers the question. Pay attention to the word in **dark print**. Fill in the circle next to the answer.*

1. A **tool** used to cut wood is a
   - ○ knife.
   - ○ saw.
   - ○ hammer.

2. What might you **collect** to recycle?
   - ○ old newspapers
   - ○ teams
   - ○ milk

3. A towel feels **damp** when you
   - ○ buy it from the store.
   - ○ use it to dry your hands.
   - ○ take it out of the closet.

4. Where might you find a lot of **soil**?
   - ○ in the air
   - ○ in the ground
   - ○ in the ocean

5. What does an **alarm** tell a firefighter to do?
   - ○ get on the fire truck
   - ○ eat lunch
   - ○ drink water

6. A cat is an **enemy** of a
   - ○ mouse.
   - ○ whale.
   - ○ seal.

7. Where might you see a **pack** of wolves?
   - ○ in a card shop
   - ○ in a box
   - ○ in a wooded area

8. What might **frighten** you?
   - ○ a sleeping baby
   - ○ a new friend
   - ○ a door slamming shut

9. It is **safe** to cross the street after you
   - ○ dash across it.
   - ○ see the signal turn red.
   - ○ look both ways.

10. What is something you might **scatter**?
    - ○ bread crumbs
    - ○ snowballs
    - ○ fish

Completing the Idea

Complete each sentence starter so that it makes sense.
*Pay attention to the word in **dark print**.*

1. When my **alarm** goes off each morning, _____

_____

2. When I go away, I **pack** _____

_____

3. A **team** of people _____

_____

4. When I **dive** into the pool, I _____

_____

5. I watch the birds **soar** over _____

_____

6. If the ice on the pond is **smooth**, _____

_____

7. My gloves are **damp** because _____

_____

8. I can **prove** that _____

_____

9. I like to **collect** _____

_____

10. A **tool** that Dad uses in the garden is _____

_____

A **prefix** is a word part that is added to the beginning of a word. A prefix changes the meaning of the word.

The prefix **un** can mean "not."	The prefix **re** can mean "again."
un + clear = unclear	**re + stack = restack**
Unclear means "not clear."	**Restack** means "to stack again."

*Write the prefix **un** or **re** to make a word that goes with the meaning shown. Then write the whole word.*

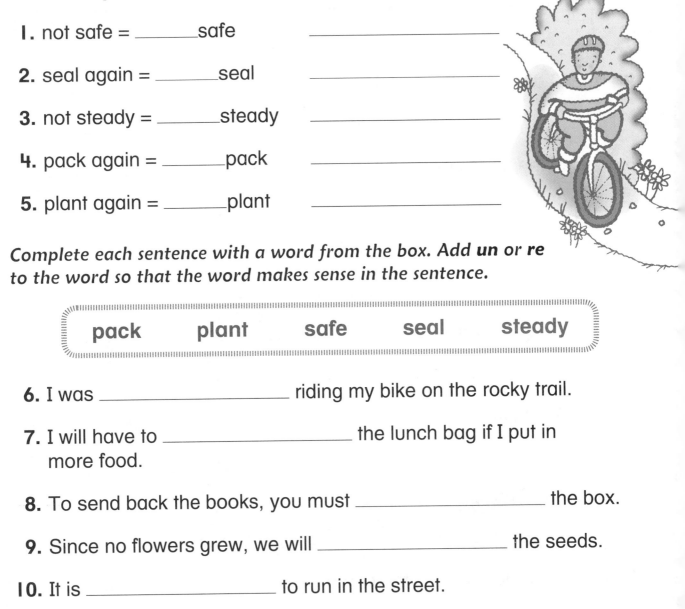

1. not safe = _____safe   _____

2. seal again = _____seal   _____

3. not steady = _____steady   _____

4. pack again = _____pack   _____

5. plant again = _____plant   _____

*Complete each sentence with a word from the box. Add **un** or **re** to the word so that the word makes sense in the sentence.*

pack	plant	safe	seal	steady

6. I was _____ riding my bike on the rocky trail.

7. I will have to _____ the lunch bag if I put in more food.

8. To send back the books, you must _____ the box.

9. Since no flowers grew, we will _____ the seeds.

10. It is _____ to run in the street.

Shades of Meaning • Analogies 2

You learned two ways in which words can go together.

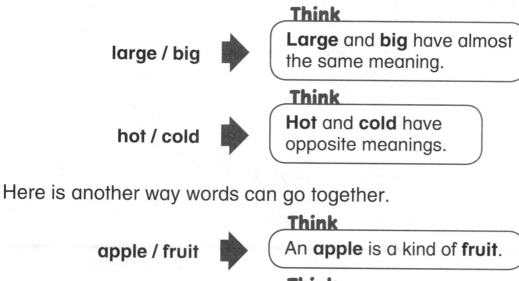

large / big → **Think** — **Large** and **big** have almost the same meaning.

hot / cold → **Think** — **Hot** and **cold** have opposite meanings.

Here is another way words can go together.

apple / fruit → **Think** — An **apple** is a kind of **fruit**.

dog / animal → **Think** — A **dog** is a kind of **animal**.

Read each pair of words. Write a sentence that tells how the words go together.

1. butterfly / insect _____

2. rake / tool _____

3. steady / shaky _____

4. cactus / plant _____

5. gather / collect _____

6. enemy / friend _____

7. soar / fly _____

8. bench / seat _____

9. search / hunt _____

Introducing the Words

Listen to this passage about a boy's experience at a school field day. Pay attention to the words in the color boxes. These are the words you will be learning in this unit.

Field Day!

(Personal Narrative)

I love to play sports at any time of the year. I'll even shiver through a soccer game in November. My favorite sports day of all is Field Day. It takes place during the last week of school. Everyone in school is on one of four teams. I am on the Blue Team.

Our teachers set up all the games before we get to school. They must wake up at dawn! They also make sure everyone is fair and plays by the rules. Yesterday, my favorite day was finally here. I couldn't wait to play and cheer for my team!

The first event of the day was an obstacle course. We had to hop through tires, run around cones, and crawl through a tube. I ran into trouble early. My foot got stuck in one of the tires. I tripped and let out a loud cry of pain. Luckily, the fall didn't do much harm. I just scraped my elbow.

Soon I was ready for the next event, the potato race. Each set of partners was given a potato on a spoon to carry back and forth across a long field of grass. To win, the partners had to go the entire way without dropping the potato. Each person had to stay calm and walk carefully. It's easy for the potato to fall off of the spoon. During my turn, I could see the potato tremble on the spoon, but it didn't drop. When I reached the finish line, I saw my partner jumping up and down. We had won the race! Our win put our team in first place. I felt like a hero!

Word Meanings

Read each word, its meaning, and the example sentence.

1. calm
(adjective)
(KAHM)

If something is **calm**, it is quiet and still.

The ducks swam on the calm lake.

🗨 Tell about something that makes you feel calm.

2. cheer
(verb)
(CHIHR)

When people **cheer**, they yell or call out loudly.

The fans cheer for the home team.

🗨 Name some events where you can hear people cheer.

3. dawn
(noun)
(DAWN)

Dawn is the time of day when the sun first comes up.

Some people wake up at dawn.

4. entire
(adjective)
(en-TIRE)

Entire means the whole thing. It is all of something.

We were so thirsty that we drank the entire jug of water.

5. fair
(adjective)
(FAIR)

A person who is **fair** follows the rules and treats everyone the same way.

Ed was fair and gave me a turn.

🗨 Tell how to share an orange in a way that is fair.

(noun)
(FAIR)

A **fair** is an outdoor place where people bring things to sell. It is a place where people have fun.

I had fun on the rides at the fair.

6. field
(noun)
(FEELD)

A **field** is an area where a game is played. Usually, a field is covered with grass.

The boy ran onto the field to join his teammates.

💬 **Tell about a game you have played on a field.**

(noun)
(FEELD)

A **field** is a large open area that has no trees. Sometimes, a field is used to grow things.

The horses ate the grass in the field.

---

7. harm
(verb)
(HARM)

Harm means "to hurt."

I stepped over the frog so that I would not harm it.

---

8. pain
(noun)
(PAYN)

A **pain** is a feeling of hurt.

I felt pain in my arm after I fell.

---

9. shiver
(verb)
(SHI-vur)

When you **shiver**, you shake quickly. Usually, your whole body will shiver if you are cold or afraid.

The cold, blowing wind made me shiver.

💬 **Act out how you would shiver on a cold day.**

---

10. tremble
(verb)
(TREM-buhl)

When you **tremble**, you shake from excitement or anger. A part of your body shakes a little when you tremble.

My fingers tremble before I play the piano for my teacher.

Match the Meaning

Choose the word from the box that matches the meaning in the clue. Write the word on the line.

| calm | cheer | entire | pain | shiver |

1. You feel this when you are hurt. _____

2. You use this word to tell about the whole thing. _____

3. You do this when you call out loudly for your team. _____

4. You feel this way when you are not upset. _____

5. You do this when you feel cold. _____

| dawn | fair | field | harm | tremble |

6. This is a grassy place where games are played. _____

7. This is what your lips might do when you feel afraid.

_____

8. This is what loud noise can do to your ears. _____

9. This is the beginning of the day. _____

10. This is where you might play games and eat apple pie.

_____

Completing the Sentence

Choose the word from the box that best completes the sentence.
Then write the word on the line.

calm	cheer	dawn	entire	fair
field	harm	pain	shiver	tremble

1. I woke up at _____ on the big day.

2. It was the day of the school _____.

3. I ran downstairs and felt a _____ in my foot.

4. I tripped over a toy, but I did not _____ my foot.

5. I passed the _____ on my way to school.

6. The _____ class was waiting for me.

7. I was so cold that I began to _____ all over.

8. The race began and I felt very _____.

9. I dashed to the finish line and everyone began to _____.

10. I was so happy that my lips began to _____.

Read the story. Then answer each question.
Use complete sentences.

Jets Win Big!

The **entire** town seemed to be at Williams Field last Friday. Why? To see if the Bears could beat the Jets one more time. It's been a bad year for the Jets. The team lost Erin Nelson in the first game. She fell and had a bad **pain** in her arm.

On Friday, the Jets remained **calm** before the game. It didn't take long to find out why. Erin Nelson ran out onto the **field**, followed by her team. Erin and the team scored goal after goal. The Bears could hear the crowd **cheer**. Then the game was over, and the score was 10–0. The Jets won **fair** and square!

1. Describe the **field** where the Bears and the Jets played the game. _____

_____

_____

2. Why do you think the Jets felt **calm** the day of the game? _____

_____

_____

3. Why did the crowd **cheer**? _____

_____

_____

4. What does it mean to win "**fair** and square"? _____

_____

_____

Write and Share

✎ *Write a story using at least five of the words in the box.*

calm	cheer	dawn	entire	fair
field	harm	pain	shiver	tremble

_____

_____

_____

_____

_____

_____

_____

_____

_____

_____

_____

_____

💬 Talk about your work with your partner to make sure you have used the words correctly. Then write one more detail to add to your story.

_____

_____

UNIT 10

Listen to this biography about two brothers who invented and flew the first engine-driven plane. Pay attention to the words in the color boxes. These are the words you will be learning in this unit.

The Wright Brothers

(Biography)

It is hard to believe that the first airplane with an engine flew just over 100 years ago. The hard work and clever thinking of Wilbur and Orville Wright made it happen.

The Wright brothers took an early interest in flying. As children, they had a toy helicopter that made them curious about flight. When the helicopter broke, the boys built their own model. That showed them not to doubt their skill at making things. As adults, the brothers built bicycles, printing presses, and kites. They also liked to make gliders, which are planes without engines.

Listen to this passage at
SadlierConnect.com.

In the 1890s, flying in gliders was dangerous. The Wright brothers were eager to make flying safer. They thought that an engine would give pilots more control.

In 1900, Orville and Wilbur went to the windy village of Kitty Hawk, North Carolina. There, they kept testing new airplane designs. Three years later, they had a model that worked. The plane was 16 feet wide and made of wood and cloth. It had a gas engine.

The first flight took off on December 17, 1903. Orville would board the plane and squeeze tightly to hold on and control the plane. The engine would start with a screech. The plane flew in the air for 120 feet. The trip lasted 12 seconds and ended with a mild crash. There was some fear that the plane was damaged, but Wilbur flew it again a few hours later. You would have to leap for joy at the sight if you had been there.

In 1905, the Wright brothers built an airplane that could fly for 30 minutes. On December 31, 1908, Wilbur flew a plane for a record-breaking 2 hours and 19 minutes. The Wright brothers kept working to build better airplanes.

Word Meanings

Read each word, its meaning, and the example sentence.

1. board
(noun)
(BORD)

A **board** is a long, flat piece of wood or plastic.

The man used the board to finish building the doghouse.

(verb)
(BORD)

If you **board** a bus, you get on it. You might also board a train or boat.

The women will board the train with their bags.

💬 Act out how you board a bus or train.

2. curious
(adjective)
(KYUR-ee-uhss)

If you are **curious**, you want to learn or find out about something.

The kitten is curious about the new goldfish.

3. dangerous
(adjective)
(DAYN-jur-uhss)

Something that is **dangerous** is not safe. It could cause harm.

Riding a bike without a helmet can be dangerous.

4. doubt
(verb)
(DOUT)

If you **doubt** something, you are not sure about it.

I doubt that their team will win today.

💬 Make a face to show you doubt something is true.

5. eager
(adjective)
(EE-gur)

A person who is **eager** is very interested in doing something.

The girl is eager to play the piano.

💬 Tell about a sport you are eager to try.

6. fear
(noun)
(FIHR)

Fear is a feeling that danger is near or that something bad will happen.

I feel fear when I am in a dark place.

(verb)
(FIHR)

If you **fear** something, you are afraid of it.

Singing in front of people is what I fear most.

💬 **Tell about an animal you would fear meeting face to face.**

7. leap
(verb)
(LEEP)

If you **leap**, you take a jump forward.

Watch the frog leap from one rock onto the other.

8. screech
(noun)
(SKREECH)

A **screech** is a loud, high sound.

The bird made a loud screech when people came into the pet store.

(verb)
(SKREECH)

When things **screech**, they make a loud sound.

The tires screech when I brake.

9. squeeze
(verb)
(SKWEEZ)

If you **squeeze** something, you hold it tightly.

The towel will dry more quickly if you squeeze the water out of it first.

💬 **Show how you squeeze a tube of toothpaste.**

10. village
(noun)
(VI-lij)

A **village** is a small town.

My grandparents live in a small village.

Match the Meaning

 Additional activities and practice with the unit words are available at SadlierConnect.com.

Choose the word from the box that matches the meaning in the clue. Write the word on the line.

> board   doubt   leap   screech   squeeze

1. You do this when you hold something tightly. _____

2. You do this when you jump forward. _____

3. You do this when you get on a train. _____

4. You do this when you are not sure about something.

   _____

5. You do this when you make a high, loud noise. _____

> curious   dangerous   eager   fear   village

6. This is what you feel when you are scared. _____

7. This word describes something that is not safe. _____

8. This word describes a person who wants to learn about something.

   _____

9. This is a small town where people live. _____

10. This word describes a person who really wants to do

    something. _____

Completing the Sentence

Choose the word from the box that best completes the sentence.
Then write the word on the line.

board	curious	dangerous	doubt	eager
fear	leap	screech	squeeze	village

1. I have always been _____ about the fish in the sea.

2. We went to a beach near a small _____.

3. A boy was paddling in the water on a long _____.

4. I was _____ to try it, too!

5. The boy said that it was not _____ at all.

6. He told me to _____ the sides with my hands.

7. Once I got into the water, I had no _____.

8. I saw a fish _____ out of the water.

9. I heard myself _____ as I fell in the cold water.

10. I do not _____ that I can learn to do it!

➽ *Read the letter. Then answer each question.*
Use complete sentences.

June 24

Dear Maria,

I took my first airplane ride, and it was great fun! The first thing we did was **board** the plane. I was **curious** about what the plane was like. A woman took me into the cockpit!

Pretty soon, the plane took off. Everything looked small from the air. I saw a **village** and lots of trees. When we landed, I heard a loud **screech**. It was the brakes! Believe me, flying is not **dangerous**. I am **eager** to do it again.

Next year, I will fly to your house. Isn't that cool?

Love,
Amelia

1. What does the phrase "**board** the plane" mean? _____

_____

_____

2. Why do you think Amelia was **curious** about what the plane was like?

_____

_____

3. What made the loud **screech** when the airplane landed? _____

_____

_____

4. Why do you think Amelia is **eager** to fly again? _____

_____

_____

Write and Share

✎ *Write a story using at least five of the words in the box.*

> board　curious　dangerous　doubt　eager
> fear　leap　screech　squeeze　village

_____

_____

_____

_____

_____

_____

_____

_____

_____

_____

_____

_____

💬 Talk about your work with your partner to make sure you have used the words correctly. Then write one more detail to add to your story.

_____

_____

Synonyms

If you need help with a word, look it up in the **Glossary** at the back of this book.

*Circle the word that has almost the <u>same</u> meaning as the word in **dark print**. Write the word on the line.*

1. We **yell** when our team wins the game.
   A. squeeze　　**B.** fear　　　　**C.** cheer　　　＿＿＿＿＿＿＿＿

2. Don't **hurt** the kittens when you pick them up.
   A. leap　　　　**B.** harm　　　　**C.** tremble　　＿＿＿＿＿＿＿＿

3. The horses are in the **meadow**.
   A. field　　　　**B.** dawn　　　　**C.** screech　　＿＿＿＿＿＿＿＿

4. I ate the **whole** cake.
   A. fair　　　　**B.** curious　　　**C.** entire　　　＿＿＿＿＿＿＿＿

5. We had fun at the **festival**.
   A. dawn　　　　**B.** fair　　　　**C.** board　　　＿＿＿＿＿＿＿＿

Antonyms

*Circle the word that has almost the <u>opposite</u> meaning as the word in **dark print**. Write the word on the line.*

1. I took a walk at **sunset**.
   A. village　　　**B.** field　　　　**C.** dawn　　　＿＿＿＿＿＿＿＿

2. I **know** I will pass the test.
   A. shiver　　　**B.** doubt　　　**C.** fear　　　＿＿＿＿＿＿＿＿

3. The car is **safe** to drive.
   A. dangerous　**B.** fair　　　　**C.** eager　　　＿＿＿＿＿＿＿＿

4. I am **nervous** when I meet my new teacher.
   A. fair　　　　**B.** entire　　　**C.** calm　　　＿＿＿＿＿＿＿＿

5. I **walk** over the puddle.
   A. squeeze　　**B.** doubt　　　**C.** leap　　　＿＿＿＿＿＿＿＿

Classifying

Look at the words in the box. Write each word in the group in which it best fits. Use each word once.

cheer	curious	eager	field
screech	shiver	squeeze	village

Words That Tell How You Feel

_____

_____

Words That Name Places

_____

_____

Sound Words

_____

_____

Action Words

_____

_____

Word Associations

Choose the answer that best completes the sentence or answers the question. Pay attention to the word in **dark print**. Fill in the circle next to the answer.

1. You might **tremble** when you
   - ○ find your socks.
   - ○ hear a big dog barking.
   - ○ play with a friend.

2. A **village** may have
   - ○ a large shopping mall.
   - ○ a few stores.
   - ○ many restaurants.

3. A cat might show **fear** by
   - ○ purring.
   - ○ eating.
   - ○ hissing.

4. You might feel **pain** in your arm if you
   - ○ eat too much food.
   - ○ throw a ball too many times.
   - ○ kick with your foot.

5. What might you do after you **board** a bus?
   - ○ find a seat
   - ○ run a race
   - ○ wait for a train

6. What might you hear at **dawn**?
   - ○ a rooster crowing
   - ○ a crowd cheering
   - ○ a school bell ringing

7. What would make you **shiver**?
   - ○ lying on a beach
   - ○ eating a sandwich
   - ○ swimming in a cold ocean

8. It woud be hard to **squeeze** a
   - ○ sponge.
   - ○ tree.
   - ○ pillow.

9. Which of these animals **screech**?
   - ○ kittens and puppies
   - ○ crows and monkeys
   - ○ whales and sharks

10. What statement would you **doubt** is true?
    - ○ Horses eat grass.
    - ○ Bears live in Alaska.
    - ○ Cows fly to the moon.

Completing the Idea

Complete each sentence starter so that it makes sense.
Pay attention to the word in **dark print.**

1. When I am **calm**, I _____

_____

2. After I read the **entire** book, I _____

_____

3. The coach was **fair** when _____

_____

4. I **tremble** when I _____

_____

5. I am **curious** about _____

_____

6. The road is **dangerous** because _____

_____

7. I **leap** when I _____

_____

8. I use a wooden **board** to _____

_____

9. In the farmer's **field**, I see _____

_____

10. I am always **eager** to _____

_____

A **suffix** is a word part that is added to the end of a word. A suffix can change the meaning of the word.

The suffix **ful** means "full of."	The suffix **less** means "without."
hope + ful = hopeful	**hope + less = hopeless**
Hopeful means "full of hope."	**Hopeless** means "without hope."
I am **hopeful** that we will win the game.	I felt **hopeless** when we were losing.

Add the suffixes **ful** and **less** to each word below.

1. harm   _____   _____

2. pain   _____   _____

3. doubt   _____   _____

4. fear   _____   _____

Add **ful** or **less** to the word in **dark print** to complete the sentence. Be sure the word makes sense in the sentence. Write the new word on the line.

5. The _____ dog jumped into the cold water and swam after the ball. **(fear)**

6. Brushing your teeth is easy and _____. **(pain)**

7. Eating poorly is _____ to your health. **(harm)**

8. We wanted it to snow, but we were _____ that it would. **(doubt)**

9. A bee is _____ if you leave it alone. **(harm)**

10. A bee sting can be _____. **(pain)**

Shades of Meaning   Word Choice 2

You learned the meaning of the word **leap** on page 109.
Look at the chart for words that are close in meaning to **leap**.
Notice how the meanings of the words are alike and different.

hop	When you **hop**, you use one or both legs to push up or forward into the air, but you don't go very far.
jump	When you **jump**, you use your legs to push up or forward with more force than a hop.
leap	When you **leap**, you take a big, strong jump forward.

Write the word from the chart that best completes each sentence.

1. We saw a dog _____ the fence.

2. Would you like to _____ rope with me?

3. A rabbit will _____ around looking for food.

4. Some frogs can _____ more than ten feet.

5. I can't _____ on one foot for very long!

*In each exercise, circle the word in **dark print** to answer the first question. Then answer the second question. Use the word you chose in your answer.*

6. Would you **hop** or **leap** to get over a large puddle? Why?

   _____

7. Would you **leap** or **hop** to move a few inches? Why?

   _____

8. Would you **jump** or **hop** on a trampoline? Why?

   _____

Introducing the Words

Listen to this biography about Margaret Heffernan Borland, one of the first women to lead a cattle drive. Pay attention to the words in the color boxes. These are the words you will be learning in this unit.

Margaret Heffernan Borland: Trail Blazer

(Biography)

In 1873, a brave Texas woman set out on a long and hard trip. Her name was Margaret Heffernan Borland. With her children and a small team of workers, Margaret led a herd of cattle from Victoria, Texas, to Wichita, Kansas. The herd had over a thousand cattle!

At the time, it was odd for a woman to lead a cattle drive. Margaret was one of the first women to do it. Many people at that time did not think it was proper for a woman to do such work. Margaret, however, was a strong woman. She did not care what others thought. She had a job to do.

Margaret's trip was tense. It was not easy. A few years earlier, cattle drivers had to carve a trail through low mountains and land covered with small trees and bushes. The trail was still rough and dangerous. It was easy to get a scrape—or worse. The tender skin of a hand or arm was no match for a thorny bush. As workers and herds of cattle traveled, the harsh sun could beam down one day. The next day, heavy rains could flood the trails.

Margaret led a type of cattle called the Texas Longhorn. A Texas Longhorn steer had very good lean meat. These cattle could survive in rough places along the trail. Texas Longhorns, however, scared easily. A coyote howling from its den could cause them to run away in a sudden rush.

The Texas Longhorns were hard to control, but Margaret made it to Wichita with most of her herd. Today, she is remembered for her independence and strength.

Word Meanings

Read each word, its meaning, and the example sentence.

1. beam
(noun)
(BEEM)

A **beam** is a long, strong piece of wood or metal that holds up part of a building.

After the builders put in the last beam, they built the roof on top.

(verb)
(BEEM)

To **beam** is to send something out.

Faraway stars beam light to Earth.

---

2. carve
(verb)
(KARV)

When you **carve** something, you cut into it.

I can carve a statue out of wood.

---

3. den
(noun)
(DEN)

A **den** is where some wild animals rest.

The wolf left its den to eat.

---

4. lean
(verb)
(LEEN)

When you **lean**, you bend in a certain direction.

Lean back to watch the night sky.

💬 **Show how you can lean to the left and to the right.**

(adjective)
(LEEN)

Something that is **lean** does not have much fat on it.

The burger had lean meat in it.

---

5. odd
(adjective)
(OD)

If something is **odd**, it is not what you are used to.

A June snowstorm would be odd.

(adjective)
(OD)

An **odd** number cannot be divided evenly by two.

Five is an odd number.

💬 **Name some examples of odd numbers.**

6. proper
(adjective)
(PROP-ur)

If something is **proper**, it is right or correct.

Wear proper clothing on cold days.

💬 Describe the proper way to act when someone is speaking.

7. scrape
(verb)
(SKRAPE)

When you **scrape** something, you rub it against a rough or sharp surface.

Help me scrape the paint off the door.

(noun)
(SKRAPE)

A **scrape** is a mark made by rubbing or scratching against something rough.

I fell and got a scrape on my knee.

8. steer
(verb)
(STIHR)

When you **steer** something, you move it in a certain direction.

I tried to steer my bike in a straight line.

💬 Name different things that people steer.

(noun)
(STIHR)

A **steer** is a bull that is raised for meat.

A steer eats grass.

9. tender
(adjective)
(TEN-dur)

When something is **tender**, it is soft and easy to cut.

Grandpa's steaks are always tender.

10. tense
(adjective)
(TENSS)

When you are **tense**, you are not relaxed.

I felt tense when I tried out for the school play.

💬 Show how you look if you are tense.

SCHOOL PLAY TRYOUTS TODAY

Match the Meaning

Additional activities and practice with the unit words are available at SadlierConnect.com.

Choose the word from the box that matches the meaning in the clue. Write the word on the line.

> lean   odd   scrape   tender   tense

1. You might feel like this before a big test. _____

2. You can do this to see past someone's head in a movie theater.

   _____

3. You can cook a carrot to make it more like this. _____

4. You might do this to a table if you drag a heavy pot across the tabletop.

   _____

5. You might use this word to describe a talking cat. _____

> beam   carve   den   proper   steer

6. This is a place where a lion sleeps at night. _____

7. This is how you make a statue out of a piece of stone.

   _____

8. This helps to hold up a skyscraper. _____

9. This is what you do to turn a car to the right or to the left.

   _____

10. This is how you might describe wearing a swimsuit to the pool.

    _____

Completing the Sentence

Choose the word from the box that best completes the sentence.
Then write the word on the line.

beam	carve	den	lean	odd
proper	scrape	steer	tender	tense

1. The move to our new house made us _____.

2. The number 3 in our address is an _____ number.

3. The small, nearby farm has goats and a _____.

4. One ceiling _____ had to be replaced after our move.

5. I had to _____ my head back to look at it.

6. A poster of a bear in its _____ is in my bedroom.

7. Mom had to _____ the paint off the kitchen table.

8. She had to pick the _____ tool to get the paint off.

9. Gloves protected the _____ skin on her hands.

10. This fall, we will _____ a turkey at our new table.

Words in Context

Read the article about sled dogs and sled drivers. Then answer each question. Use complete sentences.

Sled Dogs and Sled Drivers

Racing sled dogs is a big sport in some cold places. Dogs with thick fur and **lean** bodies are best for racing. Their lean bodies help them run quickly. Sled dogs are full of energy. Often, they are **tense** before a race starts.

During a race, the sled's blades **carve** deep lines in the snow. The driver stands in the sled to **steer** it. After the race, the drivers take care of their dogs. They check the **tender** pads on the dogs' paws. If they find a **scrape**, they clean it up so it will heal. Then they hand out treats for a job well done!

1. What does the word **lean** mean in the phrase "**lean** bodies"? _____

_____

_____

2. Why might the dogs get **tense** before a race? _____

_____

_____

3. What does it mean to **steer** a sled? _____

_____

_____

4. Why might a dog get a **scrape** on its paw? _____

_____

_____

Write and Share

✎ *Write a story using at least five of the words in the box.*

beam	carve	den	lean	odd
proper	scrape	steer	tender	tense

_____

_____

_____

_____

_____

_____

_____

_____

_____

_____

_____

💬 Talk about your work with your partner to make sure you have used the words correctly. Then write one more detail to add to your story.

_____

_____

Introducing the Words

Listen to this passage about a working guide dog.
Pay attention to the words in the color boxes.
These are the words you will be learning in this unit.

A Dog with a Job

(Informational Fiction)

My name is Penny, and I work as a guide dog. The label "guide dog" means that I help a person who is blind. I was born at Guide Dogs for the Blind in San Rafael, California. This is a place that trains puppies to be guide dogs. Years ago, the company had only one dog. The modern company of today trains hundreds of dogs every year.

When I was eight weeks old, Guide Dogs for the Blind had to select a family for me. The family gave me love and a stable home. The family members taught me good manners and how to obey commands, like "sit" and "lie down." They took me to many different places, and they played with me. Some types of play were not proper for me and were not allowed. The family members could not pitch a ball or other object for me to catch and carry back to them.

When I was eighteen months old, I went back to Guide Dogs for the Blind to begin a special training program. To be honest, I was sad to leave my family. During my training, I wore a harness. I learned how to guide a person through a busy city. I even learned fun skills like how to ride on a steep escalator. I also learned how to take a trip on a train.

Three months later, I was ready to be a guide dog. I was matched with a partner, a woman who was blind. When we met, I took a minute to sniff her hand so that I could always identify her. We trained together for three weeks. Now I have a job to do. I spend my days guiding her anywhere she wants to go. On weekends, we escape to the country, and I spend lots of time playing. I love my job.

A grown-up pup is in training at Guide Dogs for the Blind.

Puppies wear green jackets when they are getting used to different people and places.

Word Meanings

Read each word, its meaning, and the example sentence.

1. escape
(verb)
(ess-KAPE)

You **escape** to get away.

The dog tried to escape through the open gate.

---

2. honest
(adjective)
(ON-ist)

If you are **honest**, you tell the truth.

I was honest and told Dad that I lost his pen.

---

3. label
(noun)
(LAY-buhl)

A **label** is a sticker or tag fastened to something to tell more about it.

The label on the can says there is enough soup for two people.

(verb)
(LAY-buhl)

When you **label** something, you write something on a sticker or tag to tell more about the object.

We should label all our boxes so we know what is in each one.

---

4. modern
(adjective)
(MOD-urn)

When something is **modern**, it has to do with the present time.

In modern times, people write more emails than letters.

💬 Tell about a **modern** invention that you use.

---

5. object
(noun)
(OB-jikt)

An **object** is a thing that you can see or touch.

A ball is a round object.

💬 Point to a small **object**. Then point to a large one.

6. pitch
(verb)
(PICH)

When you **pitch** something, you throw it.

I tried to pitch the baseball right into the catcher's glove.

7. select
(verb)
(si-LEKT)

When you **select** something, you pick it out.

At night, I select clothes to wear the next day.

💬 **Tell how you select a book to read.**

8. sniff
(verb)
(SNIF)

When you **sniff** something, you take in air through your nose in short, quick breaths.

My rabbit likes to sniff its food.

💬 **Show how an animal might sniff the air.**

9. stable
(noun)
(STAY-buhl)

A **stable** is a building where horses are kept.

Six horses live in the stable.

(adjective)
(STAY-buhl)

Something that is **stable** is strong and not easily moved.

Mom fixed the chair leg to make it more stable.

💬 **Point to something nearby that is stable.**

10. steep
(adjective)
(STEEP)

A **steep** hill has a sharp slope that is difficult to go up.

We had to walk our bikes up the steep part of the trail.

Match the Meaning

Additional activities and practice with the unit words are available at SadlierConnect.com.

Choose the word from the box that matches the meaning in the clue. Write the word on the line.

> **escape**   **honest**   **object**   **pitch**   **sniff**

1. You would probably want a friend who is like this. _____

2. You might do this to a beautiful flower in the garden.

   _____

3. You might want to do this when you watch a boring movie.

   _____

4. You could do this with a baseball. _____

5. You might be able to hold this in your hand. _____

> **label**   **modern**   **select**   **stable**   **steep**

6. This kind of mountain would be hard to climb. _____

7. This might tell you what is in your cereal. _____

8. This word might describe a well-built bridge. _____

9. This word could describe a brand new car. _____

10. This is what you do when you pick the best apples from a

    big pile. _____

Completing the Sentence

Choose the word from the box that best completes the sentence.
Then write the word on the line.

escape	honest	label	modern	object
pitch	select	sniff	stable	steep

1. I went to a _____ to ride a horse for the first time.

2. The _____ on the trainer's shirt said, "Sue."

3. Sue helped me _____ a horse to ride.

4. She told me to let the horse _____ my hand.

5. We closed the door so the horses would not _____.

6. Some parts of the riding path were _____.

7. If the horses saw an _____ on the path, they walked around it.

8. Horseback riding is not a _____ thing to do, but it is fun.

9. After riding, I helped _____ hay to feed the horses.

10. Riding is hard work. This is the _____ truth.

Read the travel brochure. Then answer each question. Use complete sentences.

Visit the Red Horse Inn

How would you like to **escape** to the mountains? If you need a place to stay, look no further than the Red Horse Inn. We're being **honest** when we say you'll have a fun time here. Visitors use the **labels "modern"** and "clean" to describe our rooms. If you need a toothbrush or a towel, just let us know. We can bring you the **object** you need. As you may have guessed from our name, we have a **stable** on our grounds. You can go horseback riding every day if you want! We also have flat and **steep** hiking trails. Just **select** what you like best!

1. What does the **label "modern"** tell you about the rooms? _____

_____

_____

2. What is one **object** the workers at the inn could bring to you? _____

_____

_____

3. What would you find in the **stable** at the Red Horse Inn? _____

_____

_____

4. Which is harder to hike, a flat trail or a **steep** trail? _____

_____

_____

Write and Share

✎ *Write a story using at least five of the words in the box.*

escape	honest	label	modern	object
pitch	select	sniff	stable	steep

_____

_____

_____

_____

_____

_____

_____

_____

_____

💬 Talk about your work with your partner to make sure you have used the words correctly. Then write one more detail to add to your story.

_____

_____

Synonyms

Circle the word that has almost the *same* meaning as the word in **dark print.** *Write the word on the line.*

1. It would be **strange** to have a bear as a pet.
   A. tense   **B.** honest   **C.** odd   _____

2. Can you **toss** the ball to me?
   A. beam   **B.** pitch   **C.** carve   _____

3. You can **pick** the pen you like best.
   A. scrape   **B.** select   **C.** sniff   _____

4. We saw a young **bull** at the farm.
   A. steer   **B.** label   **C.** den   _____

5. We cooked the potatoes until they were **soft**.
   A. honest   **B.** tense   **C.** tender   _____

Antonyms

Circle the word that has almost the *opposite* meaning as the word in **dark print.** *Write the word on the line.*

1. The road is very **flat**.
   A. proper   **B.** modern   **C.** steep   _____

2. This animal has a **fat** body.
   A. lean   **B.** stable   **C.** proper   _____

3. I felt **relaxed** at the beach.
   A. tense   **B.** steep   **C.** modern   _____

4. The house is very **old**.
   A. odd   **B.** modern   **C.** proper   _____

5. My chair is **shaky**.
   A. stable   **B.** lean   **C.** tender   _____

REVIEW UNITS 11–12

Look at the words in the box. Write each word in the group in which it best fits. Use each word once.

den   escape   honest   lean
pitch   proper   stable   tender

Places Where Animals Live

_____

_____

Words That Tell About Meat

_____

_____

Action Words

_____

_____

Words That Tell About Your Behavior

_____

_____

Choose the answer that best completes the sentence or answers the question. Pay attention to the word in **dark print**. Fill in the circle next to the answer.

1. Why might you **label** your notebook?
   - ○ because it's blue
   - ○ so people know it's yours
   - ○ because you don't like it

2. What is an **odd** thing to do with your hand?
   - ○ draw a picture
   - ○ score a goal in soccer
   - ○ play piano

3. Where might you find a **beam**?
   - ○ in a house
   - ○ in a bowl of cereal
   - ○ in a lake

4. To make sure a pet mouse doesn't **escape**, you should
   - ○ clean out its cage.
   - ○ make sure it takes naps.
   - ○ close the door to its cage.

5. Which of these is something you **steer**?
   - ○ a farm
   - ○ an apple
   - ○ a bike

6. Which of these is a **modern** thing?
   - ○ a horse
   - ○ the Internet
   - ○ a tree

7. What might you find in a **den**?
   - ○ a baseball field
   - ○ a whale
   - ○ a sleeping wolf

8. What might cause you to **scrape** your elbow?
   - ○ falling on the sidewalk
   - ○ watching TV
   - ○ wearing a sweatshirt

9. If you feel **tense**, you
   - ○ are great at sports.
   - ○ are not calm.
   - ○ own more than nine things.

10. If a house is **stable**, it will
   - ○ stand for a long time.
   - ○ fall over.
   - ○ have to be painted red.

Completing the Idea

Complete each sentence starter so that it makes sense.
*Pay attention to the word in **dark print**.*

1. The **label** on the can said that _____

_____

2. When I see the sun **beam** through my window, I _____

_____

3. My favorite **object** in my room is _____

_____

4. It was **odd** to find _____

_____

5. I felt **tense** when _____

_____

6. If I **lean** my head back, I can see _____

_____

7. It is not **proper** to _____

_____

8. At the supermarket, I **select** _____

_____

9. I got a **scrape** when I _____

_____

10. I like to **sniff** _____

_____

A **multiple-meaning word** is a word with more than one meaning.

> **board 1.** *(noun)* a long, flat piece of wood or plastic **2.** *(verb)* to get on a vehicle such as a ship, plane, or train
>
> This sentence shows the second meaning (meaning 2) of **board**:
>
> We **board** the bus at 12 noon.

Write the word that completes each sentence. Then write 1 or 2 to show which meaning of the word is used.

> **beam 1.** *(noun)* a long, strong piece of wood or metal that holds up part of a building **2.** *(verb)* to send something out

_____ **1.** Use a flashlight to _____ the light on the path.

_____ **2.** We need another _____ to hold up the roof.

> **odd 1.** *(adjective)* not what you are used to **2.** *(adjective)* cannot be divided evenly by two

_____ **3.** The number 11 is an _____ number.

_____ **4.** I find it _____ that you are here so early.

> **steer 1.** *(verb)* to move something in a certain direction **2.** *(noun)* a bull that is raised for meat

_____ **5.** Mom will _____ the car around the bus.

_____ **6.** The _____ won first prize at the state fair.

Shades of Meaning Words That Describe Food

The word **lean** can mean "thin" or "without fat." It is often used to describe meat. Look at the chart for other words that can be used to tell about food. Think about how the words help you to imagine what a food is like.

lean	**Lean** meat does not have much fat.
spicy	**Spicy** foods have a strong flavor because there are many spices in them. They can make your mouth feel hot.
juicy	**Juicy** foods are full of juice and flavor.

Write the name of each food next to the word that best describes it.

chili   hot pepper   skinless chicken

peach   orange   sliced turkey

lean 1. _____   2. _____

spicy 3. _____   4. _____

juicy 5. _____   6. _____

Complete each sentence so that it makes sense. Use the word **lean**, **spicy**, *or* **juicy** *in your answer.*

7. My hands were a sweet, sticky mess after_____

_____.

8. My mouth was on fire after_____

_____.

9. To become more healthy, my brother exercised and_____

_____.

Introducing the Words

Listen to this fairy tale about a girl who wanders into the home of three bears. Pay attention to the words in the color boxes. These are the words you will be learning in this unit.

Goldilocks and the Bear Family

(Fairy Tale)

Mama Bear, Papa Bear, and Little Bear lived in a big hollow tree in the forest. Papa Bear was an expert at cooking. One day, he made a very tasty soup.

"While we wait for our soup to cool," Mama Bear said, "let's walk to the post office and mail this letter." Mama Bear wrote an address on the letter. Little Bear found a stamp.

Soon after the bears left, a girl named Goldilocks walked down the forest path and right into their house!

"Ooh, soup," Goldilocks said in delight. She tasted from the first bowl. It was too hot. The second was too cold. The third was *just right,* and she ate the whole thing!

Then Goldilocks went into the living room, where she saw three books. The first book was too long. The second was too short. Goldilocks picked up the third book. "This book is *just long enough.*"

Goldilocks read the first section of the book, but then it became difficult for her to stay awake. "I need to go relax," she yawned.

Goldilocks tried the beds. Papa Bear's bed was too hard. Mama Bear's was too soft. Little Bear's was *just perfect.*

When the bears got home, they could tell that someone had been there. They were not happy.

"Someone bent the pages of my book," Little Bear cried, "and that person ate my soup, too!"

Just then, the bears heard snoring. When they walked into the bedroom, Goldilocks woke up with a start.

She tried to make an excuse. "I was just watching the house while you were gone," she stammered.

The bears would not accept this. "You can't walk into someone's home without asking," they roared. "Please leave!"

Goldilocks dashed out quickly. She never bothered the bears again.

Word Meanings

Read each word, its meaning, and the example sentence.

1. accept
(verb)
(ak-SEPT)

When you **accept** something, you take or receive it.

The company will accept packages between 9:00 A.M. and 3:00 P.M.

🗩 Act out how you accept a gift.

2. address
(noun)
(AD-ress)

An **address** tells where a person or business is located.

The address is 43 Grand Street, Houston, TX.

🗩 Tell about a place where you can see an address.

(verb)
(uh-DRESS)

If you **address** people or groups, you speak to them.

Speak clearly and loudly when you address the audience.

3. difficult
(adjective)
(DIF-i-kuhlt)

Something that is **difficult** is hard to do or understand.

It is difficult to play chess well.

🗩 Tell about a time you did something difficult.

4. excuse
(noun)
(ek-SKYOOSS)

An **excuse** is a reason that explains a mistake.

My excuse for being late is that I overslept.

(verb)
(ek-SKYOOZ)

When you **excuse** another person, you forgive the person.

Please excuse me for bumping into you!

5. expert
(noun)
(EK-spurt)

An **expert** is someone who knows a lot about some special thing or does something really well.

Grandma Moses was an expert painter.

💬 Tell what kind of expert you would like to be.

6. hollow
(adjective)
(HOL-oh)

Something **hollow** has a hole or an empty space inside.

The owl lives in a hollow tree trunk.

7. relax
(verb)
(ri-LAKS)

When you **relax**, you become less tense.

A back rub can relax tight muscles.

💬 Describe what you do to relax.

8. section
(noun)
(SEK-shuhn)

A **section** is part of a whole.

I never read the sports section.

9. stamp
(noun)
(STAMP)

A **stamp** is a small piece of printed paper that shows when postage is paid.

The letter was returned because it did not have a stamp.

(verb)
(STAMP)

If you **stamp** your foot, you put your foot down with force.

The camper will stamp out the fire so it doesn't spread.

10. whole
(adjective)
(HOLE)

Something **whole** is complete. It has all its parts.

We could not eat the whole pizza.

Match the Meaning

Additional activities and practice with the unit words are available at SadlierConnect.com.

Choose the word from the box that matches the meaning in the clue. Write the word on the line.

accept	address	difficult	relax	whole

1. You write this information on an envelope. _____

2. You might do this if someone gives you a package. _____

3. You try to do this on vacation. _____

4. You would eat this amount of a sandwich when you are hungry.

_____

5. You might describe juggling five balls this way. _____

excuse	expert	hollow	section	stamp

6. This might be what you tell a teacher if you don't do your homework.

_____

7. This person might teach a class. _____

8. This word can describe a cave or a straw. _____

9. This is what you put on an envelope to send a letter.

_____

10. This word names one part of a book or newspaper. _____

Completing the Sentence

Choose the word from the box that best completes the sentence.
Then write the word on the line.

accept	address	difficult	excuse	expert
hollow	relax	section	stamp	whole

1. It is not _____ to mail a package.

2. Here is how to send one like an _____.

3. Follow these steps, and there will be no _____ for problems.

4. First, put the _____ set of objects in a large box.

5. Fill in any _____ spaces with crumpled newspaper.

6. Tape the box well to close it. Write the _____ on top.

7. Find the upper right _____ on the top of the box.

8. That is where the _____ or postage sticker will go.

9. Take the package to the post office, and _____.

10. In a few days, the person should receive and _____ the package.

Words in Context

Read the restaurant review. Then answer each question. Use complete sentences.

The Corner Diner

Last week, this reviewer had dinner at The Corner Diner. I had many problems when I ate there. The host seated me in a **section** near the kitchen. It was **difficult** to get help from the waiter. I thought I would have to **stamp** my feet to get attention. The staff made one **excuse** after another. The chef is an **expert** who has worked at many famous restaurants. Still, the food did not taste good. My piece of chicken was tough and dry. The dumplings were **hollow** instead of packed with vegetables. I was disappointed with the **whole** meal. If you want good food, go somewhere else.

1. How can you get someone's attention without **stamping** your feet?

_____

_____

2. How did the reviewer feel about the **excuses** the staff made? _____

_____

_____

3. What makes the chef at The Corner Diner an **expert**? _____

_____

_____

4. Why does the reviewer complain about the **hollow** dumplings? _____

_____

_____

Write and Share

✎ *Write a story using at least five of the words in the box.*

accept	address	difficult	excuse	expert
hollow	relax	section	stamp	whole

_____

_____

_____

_____

_____

_____

_____

_____

_____

_____

_____

_____

_____

_____

💬 Talk about your work with your partner to make sure you have used the words correctly. Then write one more detail to add to your story.

_____

_____

UNIT 14

Listen to this article about train travel. Pay attention to the words in the color boxes. These are the words you will be learning in this unit.

One Great Way to Travel

(Magazine Article)

All aboard! All over the world, train travel is a major way for people to get around. Before there were trains, horse-drawn coaches and boats were the common ways for people to travel. Trains are much faster. They move on tracks made of steel rails. Trains also have railroad cars that attach to each other. This allows trains to carry many people at one time.

Today, we also have cars, buses, and planes for travel. However, the train is still a big part of our lives. The United States has a very large railway system. It has enough track to circle the earth five times! We are not the only country with these different ways of traveling. Other countries have similar ways to travel, too.

There are different kinds of trains. Some are commuter trains that people take to work every day. Commuter trains can fill up very quickly in the morning and early evening. These are the times when most people travel to and from work. Trains can be so crowded that people have to stand and hold on to a handle or a pole. Sometimes, there is only room for a very slender person.

Another kind of train takes people long distances. These trains sell only as many tickets as there are seats. That way, each passenger has a seat. Many trains that travel long distances have separate cars where people can eat and sleep.

Some people prepare for long train rides by packing books to read or games to play. Other people like to spend the ride taking in the sights. If this is what you choose to do, simply sit back and admire the scenery. Your only task is to enjoy the ride!

Read each word, its meaning, and the example sentence.

1. admire
(verb)
(ad-MIRE)

When you **admire** someone or something, you think highly of the person or thing.

The players admire the coach because she is smart and kind.

💬 Tell about a famous person you admire.

2. attach
(verb)
(uh-TACH)

If you **attach** something, you join or connect it.

Use tape to attach the note to the door.

3. handle
(noun)
(HAN-duhl)

The **handle** of an object is the part you use to lift or hold it.

Pull hard on the handle to open the door.

(verb)
(HAN-duhl)

If you **handle** a problem, you take care of it.

A plumber can handle the problem of your leaky pipe.

4. major
(adjective)
(MAY-jur)

Something **major** is important or great in size or number.

Heavy rain was a major cause of the flood.

5. passenger
(noun)
(PASS-uhn-jur)

A **passenger** is someone who travels in a vehicle but is not the driver.

The passenger fell asleep in the car.

💬 Name some places where you can find passengers.

6. prepare
(verb)
(pri-PAIR)

To **prepare** is to get ready.

We will prepare for the birthday party by getting hats, candles, and cake.

💬 **Tell what you do to prepare for bedtime.**

---

7. separate
(verb)
(SEP-uh-rate)

When you **separate** things, you sort or set them apart.

Please separate the dark and light clothes before putting them in the washing machine.

(adjective)
(SEP-ur-it)

Separate objects are set apart. They are not joined.

The two sisters have separate bedrooms.

---

8. similar
(adjective)
(SIM-uh-lur)

If two things are **similar**, they are alike or much the same.

It is hard to tell the two drinks apart because they have a similar taste.

💬 **Point out two objects that are similar in size.**

---

9. slender
(adjective)
(SLEN-dur)

A **slender** person or thing is thin.

The slender tree branches snapped off in the storm.

---

10. task
(noun)
(TASK)

A **task** is a job to be done.

Each weekend during the fall, my task is to rake the leaves.

💬 **Tell about a task that you help do at home.**

Match the Meaning

 Additional activities and practice with the unit words are available at **SadlierConnect.com.**

Choose the word from the box that matches the meaning in the clue. Write the word on the line.

> admire   attach   handle   prepare   separate

1. You pull this to open a door. _____

2. You do this to a beautiful painting or a hero. _____

3. You can use glue or tape to do this. _____

4. You might do this to clothes when you pack them away for different seasons. _____

5. You should do this before a trip. _____

> major   passenger   similar   slender   task

6. This is how a person on a diet wants to look. _____

7. This is work such as cleaning or sweeping that needs to be done.

   _____

8. This word tells how two hats might look. _____

9. This is one of many people who sit in a car, bus, train, or plane.

   _____

10. This word describes a big or important part of something.

    _____

Completing the Sentence

Choose the word from the box that best completes the sentence.
Then write the word on the line.

admire	attach	handle	major	passenger
prepare	separate	similar	slender	task

1. A plane's emergency landing turned a _____ into a hero.

2. The woman did an important _____ that saved the day.

3. It was a good thing she read the manual to _____.

4. She was ready for the _____ job of opening the emergency back door.

5. A flight attendant did a _____ thing at the front of the plane.

6. The woman had to _____ a panel from the wall.

7. She could then turn the _____ to unlock the door.

8. Even though she was _____, she could lift the door.

9. Finally, she was able to _____ an escape slide.

10. All of the people on the plane _____ what she did.

⬇ *Read the fantasy story. Then answer each question. Use complete sentences.*

The Space Trip

Anna was excited about her first ride into space. She climbed into the spaceship and took a seat. Another **passenger** was already on board. He had blue skin, four arms, and no hair. A wall **separated** the passengers from the robot pilots. One pilot said, "**Prepare** for launch! Fasten your seat belts!" It then pulled a **handle** with three **slender** fingers. As the spaceship zoomed up, Anna's body pressed hard against the seat. Earth looked as small as a dot behind her. Soon the sky was black and full of stars. Anna leaned forward to **admire** the view. It was like nothing she had ever seen before.

1. Is the other **passenger** on the trip a person from Earth? Explain. _____

_____

_____

2. Which groups on the spaceship does the wall **separate**? _____

_____

_____

3. How do the passengers **prepare** for launch? _____

_____

_____

4. How would you describe the **handle** that the pilot pulls? _____

_____

_____

✎ *Write a story using at least five of the words in the box.*

admire	attach	handle	major	passenger
prepare	separate	similar	slender	task

_____

_____

_____

_____

_____

_____

_____

_____

_____

_____

_____

💬 Talk about your work with your partner to make sure you have used the words correctly. Then write one more detail to add to your story.

_____

_____

Synonyms

Circle the word that has almost the same meaning as the word in **dark print**. Write the word on the line.

1. Please **stick** this label on the box.
   A. separate   **B.** prepare   **C.** attach   _____

2. The two hats I bought today are **alike**.
   A. similar   **B.** major   **C.** whole   _____

3. The hotel guests can **rest** by the pool.
   A. relax   **B.** separate   **C.** attach   _____

4. The first **job** is to rake the leaves.
   A. task   **B.** handle   **C.** excuse   _____

5. I will **plan** for the trip.
   A. address   **B.** prepare   **C.** admire   _____

Antonyms

Circle the word that has almost the opposite meaning as the word in **dark print**. Write the word on the line.

1. Lightning is a **minor** problem.
   A. hollow   **B.** major   **C.** similar   _____

2. Many people **dislike** the speaker.
   A. accept   **B.** prepare   **C.** admire   _____

3. The two teams will ride in the **same** buses.
   A. separate   **B.** slender   **C.** whole   _____

4. I **reject** your offer.
   A. stamp   **B.** relax   **C.** accept   _____

5. There was a **stuffed** piñata at the party.
   A. difficult   **B.** hollow   **C.** slender   _____

Classifying

Look at the words in the box. Write each word in the group in which it best fits. Use each word once.

> address   difficult   expert   passenger
> section   slender   stamp   whole

Words That Name Kinds of People

_____

_____

Words About the Mail

_____

_____

Words That Name Parts

_____

_____

Describing Words

_____

_____

Word Associations

*Choose the answer that best completes the sentence or answers the question. Pay attention to the word in **dark print**. Fill in the circle next to the answer.*

1. You might use a **handle** to
   - ○ open a door.
   - ○ cut a rope.
   - ○ write a story.

2. Where would you find a **passenger**?
   - ○ at the beach
   - ○ in a school
   - ○ on a train

3. It is **difficult** to
   - ○ lift a paper plate.
   - ○ climb a mountain.
   - ○ walk a dog.

4. You might eat a **whole** pizza if you are
   - ○ hungry.
   - ○ bored.
   - ○ tired.

5. How would you **prepare** dinner?
   - ○ by cooking it
   - ○ by eating it
   - ○ by cleaning it up

6. Which activity would most help a person **relax**?
   - ○ doing homework
   - ○ taking a nap
   - ○ cleaning the attic

7. You would **excuse** yourself from a party if you
   - ○ were having fun.
   - ○ felt sick.
   - ○ liked the music.

8. What is a **major** part of a sandwich?
   - ○ mustard
   - ○ lettuce
   - ○ bread

9. Which object is most **similar** to a pencil?
   - ○ paper
   - ○ eraser
   - ○ pen

10. Which object is **hollow**?
    - ○ plate
    - ○ spoon
    - ○ straw

Completing the Idea

Complete each sentence starter so that it makes sense.
*Pay attention to the word in **dark print**.*

1. I most **admire** _____

_____

2. My favorite **section** of the neighborhood is _____

_____

3. When I grow up, I want to be an **expert** in _____

_____

4. I **prepare** each day for school because _____

_____

5. The **task** I like least is _____

_____

6. I find it **difficult** to _____

_____

7. My **address** is _____

_____

8. I **relax** when _____

_____

9. A **major** part of my day is spent _____

_____

10. The person I am most **similar** to is _____

_____

When you read, you may come across words that you do not know. Sometimes, the other words in the sentence can help you figure out the meaning of the word.

> I was **absent** from school because I was sick.

In this sentence, the words **I was sick** give a clue to the meaning of the word **absent**.

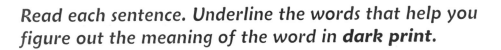

*Read each sentence. Underline the words that help you figure out the meaning of the word in **dark print**.*

1. A **boulder** is a large, round rock.

2. I like to **munch** on peanuts and popcorn at the movies.

3. The sun will **disappear** behind the clouds.

4. We sat in a **cozy** spot by the fireplace.

5. Too much salt can **spoil** the soup.

Circle the word that best completes each sentence. Underline the words that helped you make your choice.

6. We stood on the (**stage**, **lake**) to sing our song.

7. The baby slept quietly in the (**leaf**, **cradle**).

8. Please buy some milk and apples at the (**market**, **cow**).

Shades of Meaning Word Choice 3

You learned the meaning of **slender** on page 153. Look at the chart for words that are close in meaning to **slender**. Notice how the meanings of the words are alike and different.

slender	When someone or something is **slender**, that person or thing is thin but still healthy or strong.
skinny	A **skinny** object is very thin. A **skinny** person has little fat or muscle.
scrawny	When someone or something is **scrawny**, that person or thing may be weak from being too thin.

Write the word from the chart that best completes each sentence.

1. Dad is _____ because he gets a lot of exercise.

2. We used long, _____ sticks to roast marshmallows.

3. A flamingo is a pink bird with long, _____ legs.

4. This _____ chicken wing has hardly any meat on it.

5. Her arms are _____, but they can lift the heavy box.

6. When I found the puppy, it was _____ and dirty.

Read each clue. Write the word that goes with each clue.
Choose from slender, skinny, or scrawny.

7. someone who is fit and in good shape _____

8. a stray, or homeless, cat _____

9. a healthy person who wants to build muscle _____

Match the Meaning

Choose the word that best matches the meaning.
Fill in the circle next to the word.

1. to make someone afraid
   ○ notice   ○ steer   ○ prepare   ○ frighten

2. to join one thing to another
   ○ attach   ○ separate   ○ address   ○ pitch

3. to receive something
   ○ scrape   ○ escape   ○ label   ○ accept

4. to get on
   ○ signal   ○ scatter   ○ board   ○ pack

5. to tell that something bad may happen
   ○ squeeze   ○ whisper   ○ carve   ○ warn

6. to shake
   ○ prove   ○ screech   ○ tremble   ○ seal

7. a group of animals
   ○ tool   ○ herd   ○ handle   ○ task

8. to jump forward
   ○ shiver   ○ leap   ○ soar   ○ beam

9. a large area without trees
   ○ soil   ○ stable   ○ field   ○ den

10. wet or moist
   ○ damp   ○ dangerous   ○ smooth   ○ calm

Completing the Sentence

Choose the word that best completes the sentence.
Fill in the circle next to the word.

11. Only 500 people live in the _____.
    ○ team   ○ village   ○ passenger   ○ whole

12. The traffic light helps bikers and drivers stay _____.
    ○ safe   ○ steady   ○ slender   ○ similar

13. My brother and I _____ different rocks.
    ○ plant   ○ cheer   ○ collect   ○ harm

14. I woke up at _____.
    ○ pain   ○ object   ○ dawn   ○ section

15. The insect I _____ most is the bee.
    ○ excuse   ○ fear   ○ relax   ○ sniff

16. The hill is too _____ to climb.
    ○ entire   ○ steep   ○ tender   ○ eager

17. My friend is _____ and always tells the truth.
    ○ honest   ○ difficult   ○ hollow   ○ tense

18. Seabirds _____ in the water for fish.
    ○ chew   ○ dive   ○ doubt   ○ lean

19. I am very _____ about snakes and turtles.
    ○ major   ○ fair   ○ proper   ○ curious

20. I know that a fly is an _____ because it has six legs.
    ○ insect   ○ island   ○ alarm   ○ enemy

Vocabulary for Comprehension

Read this passage about a popular hobby, stamp collecting.
Then answer the questions.

U.S. stamps from the past

A Fun Hobby

Do you know what a *philatelist* is? It's a **stamp** collector. Stamp collecting has been around for a long time. In the United States, the first stamps were sold in 1847. One had a picture of Benjamin Franklin. Another had a picture of George Washington. **Modern** stamps have all kinds of pictures, from movie stars to cartoons.

Are you **eager** to become a stamp collector? You do not have to be an **expert** to be one. You can start by saving stamps from your family's mail. Then you can put them in a binder. You may pick a stamp because you **admire** the person or place it shows. You can **select** stamps that you think are **odd**, or unusual. Each stamp is special in its own way. That is what makes collecting stamps such a fun hobby.

Choose the answer that best completes the sentence or answers the question. Fill in the circle next to the answer.

21. This passage is mostly about
    ○ the history of stamps.
    ○ the year 1847.
    ○ stamp collecting.

22. In this passage, the word **stamp** means
    ○ to mark something with ink.
    ○ to push your foot down hard.
    ○ a piece of paper put on mail.

23. What does the word **modern** mean?
    ○ past time
    ○ present time
    ○ future time

24. What does the word **eager** mean?
    ○ forgetting to do something
    ○ asking to do something
    ○ wanting to do something

25. What is an **expert**?
    ○ someone who knows a lot
    ○ someone who makes stamps
    ○ someone who collects stamps

26. The word **admire** means
    ○ to collect something.
    ○ to think highly of.
    ○ to arrive somewhere.

27. What is another word for **select**?
    ○ pick
    ○ cross
    ○ stack

28. In this passage, the word **odd** means
    ○ bright.
    ○ normal.
    ○ different.

29. What word from the passage helps you know the meaning of **odd**?
    ○ modern
    ○ unusual
    ○ fun

30. The author most likely wrote this passage to
    ○ tell why we use stamps.
    ○ give facts about stamp collecting.
    ○ tell which stamps are the best.

In this glossary, each unit word is followed by its **pronunciation**. The pronunciation tells you how to say the word.

An **abbreviation** is a short way of writing a word. Here are some abbreviations you will find in this glossary.

n. noun   **adj.** adjective   **v.** verb   **adv.** adverb

GLOSSARY

Aa

accept (ak sept') (ak-SEPT)
(v.) to take or receive something

address
1. (n.) (ad' res) (AD-ress) where a person or business is located
2. (v.) (ə dres') (uh-DRESS) to speak to a person or group

admire (ad mīr') (ad-MIRE)
(v.) to think highly of a person or thing

agree (ə grē') (uh-GREE)
(v.) to think the same way someone else thinks

alarm (ə lärm') (uh-LARM)
(n.) something that wakes people or warns them of danger, such as a bell or a buzzer

arrive (ə rīv') (uh-RIVE)
(v.) to reach the place you set out for

attach (ə tach') (uh-TACH)
(v.) to join or connect something

Bb

bare (bâr) (BAIR)
(adj.) not covered

beach (bēch) (BEECH)
(n.) a strip of land near the water that is usually sandy

beam (bēm) (BEEM)
1. (n.) a long, strong piece of wood or metal that holds up part of a building
2. (v.) to send something out over a long distance

bench (bench) (BENCH)
(n.) a long, narrow seat for a few people to sit on

board (bôrd) (BORD)
1. (n.) a long, thin, flat piece of wood or plastic
2. (v.) to get on something

branch (branch) (BRANCH)
(n.) a part of a tree that grows out from its trunk

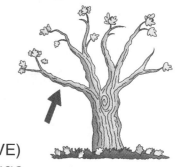

brave (brāv) (BRAVE)
(adj.) having courage and not being afraid of danger

bridge (brij) (BRIJ)
(*n.*) a structure above and across water or a road. People or cars can go over it to get to the other side.

bright (brīt) (BRITE)
1. (*adj.*) giving off a lot of light
2. (*adj.*) shiny

Cc

calm (käm) (KAHM)
(*adj.*) quiet and still

carve (kärv) (KARV)
(*v.*) to cut into something

center (sen′ tər) (SEN-tur)
(*n.*) a place that is in the middle of something

cheer (chēr) (CHIHR)
(*v.*) to yell or call out loudly

chew (chü) (CHOO)
(*v.*) to break into small pieces with teeth

clear (klēr) (KLIHR)
1. (*adj.*) not cloudy or dark
2. (*adj.*) easy to see through

collect (kə lekt′) (kuh-LEKT)
(*v.*) to gather things together

cross (krôs) (KRAWSS)
1. (*v.*) to go from one side to another
2. (*adj.*) angry or not pleased

crowd (kraúd) (KROUD)
(*n.*) a lot of people all together

curious (kyúr′ ē əs) (KYUR-ee-uhss)
(*adj.*) wanting to find out about something

Dd

damp (damp) (DAMP)
(*adj.*) a little wet or moist

dangerous (dān′ jər əs) (DAYN-jur-uhss)
(*adj.*) not safe

dash (dash) (DASH)
1. (*v.*) to move quickly
2. (*n.*) a small amount of something

dawn (dôn) (DAWN)
(*n.*) the time of day when the sun first comes up

deep (dēp) (DEEP)
(*adj.*) a long way down

den (den) (DEN)
(*n.*) a place where some kinds of wild animals go to rest

difficult (dif′ i kult) (DIF-i-kuhlt)
(*adj.*) hard to do or understand

dive (dīv) (DIVE)
(*v.*) to go head first into water with your arms stretched out in front

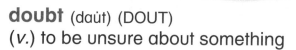

doubt (daút) (DOUT)
(*v.*) to be unsure about something

Ee

eager (ē′ gər) (EE-gur)
(*adj.*) wanting to do something a lot

enemy (e′ nə mē) (E-nuh-mee)
(*n.*) an animal or person who doesn't like, or wants to harm, another animal or person

enormous (ē nôr′ məs)
(ee-NOR-muhss)
(*adj.*) very big

entire (en tīr′) (en-TIRE)
(*adj.*) all of something

escape (es kāp′) (ess-KAPE)
(*v.*) to get away from someone or something

evening (ēv′ niŋ) (EEV-ning)
(*n.*) the part of the day between afternoon and night

exactly (ig zakt′ lē) (ig-ZAKT-lee)
(*adv.*) happening in the same way

excuse
1. (*n.*) (ek skūs′) (ek-SKYOOSS)
a reason that explains a mistake
2. (*v.*) (ek skūz′) (ek-SKYOOZ) to forgive

expert (ek′ spûrt) (EK-spurt)
(*n.*) someone who knows a lot about some special thing or does something really well

Ff

fair (fâr) (FAIR)
1. (*adj.*) going by the rules and treating everyone the same
2. (*n.*) an outdoor place where people sell things. It is a place where people have fun.

famous (fā′ məs) (FAY-muhss)
(*adj.*) well-known by many people

fear (fēr) (FIHR)
1. (*n.*) a feeling that danger is near or that something bad might happen
2. (*v.*) to be afraid of

feast (fēst) (FEEST)
(*n.*) a very large meal on a special day

field (fēld) (FEELD)
1. (*n.*) a grassy area where a game is played
2. (*n.*) a large area without trees

finally (fī′ nəl ē) (FYE-nuhl-ee)
(*adv.*) at last

float (flōt) (FLOHT)
(*v.*) to stay on top of water or in the air

flour (flaủr) (FLOUR)
(*n.*) grain that is ground into powder and used for baking

forest (fôr′ ist) (FOR-ist)
(*n.*) a large area with many trees

fresh (fresh) (FRESH)
1. (*adj.*) clean or new
2. (*adj.*) cool or refreshing

frighten (frī′ tən) (FRYE-tuhn)
(*v.*) to scare someone

frown (fraủn) (FROUN)
1. (*v.*) to move your eyebrows together and wrinkle your forehead if unhappy or annoyed
2. (*n.*) an unhappy look on your face

Gg

gentle (jen′ təl) (JEN-tuhl)
(*adj.*) soft and mild

greedy (grē′ dē) (GREE-dee)
(*adj.*) wanting more of something than what is needed

Hh

handle (han′ dəl) (HAN-duhl)
1. (*n.*) the part of something you use to lift or hold it
2. (*v.*) to take care of something

harm (härm) (HARM)
(*v.*) to hurt

herd (hûrd) (HURD)
(*n.*) a group of animals that may feed or travel together

hero (hir′ ō) (HIHR-oh)
(*n.*) a person who is brave and does good things

hollow (häl′ ō) (HOL-oh)
(*adj.*) having a hole or an empty space inside

honest (än′ ist) (ON-ist)
(*adj.*) when you tell the truth

hour (aủr) (OUR)
(*n.*) a unit of time that is sixty minutes long

Ii

idea (ī dē′ ə) (eye-DEE-uh)
(*n.*) a thought or a plan. An idea is something that you think of.

inn (in) (IN)
(*n.*) a small place where people can rent rooms and stay for the night

insect (in′ sekt) (IN-sekt)
(*n.*) a tiny animal with three main body parts, three pairs of legs, one or two pairs of wings, and no backbone. Ants and beetles are insects.

island (ī′ lənd) (EYE-luhnd)
(*n.*) land that has water all around it

GLOSSARY

Ll

label (lā′ bəl) (LAY-buhl)
1. (*n.*) a sticker or tag fastened to something to tell more about it
2. (*v.*) to write something on a sticker or tag to tell more about the object

leader (lē′ dər) (LEE-dur)
(*n.*) a person who shows people where to go or how to do something

lean (lēn) (LEEN)
1. (*v.*) to bend in a certain direction
2. (*adj.*) having little fat

leap (lēp) (LEEP)
(*v.*) to take a jump forward

Mm

major (mā′ jər) (MAY-jur)
(*adj.*) important or great in size or number

midnight (mid′ nīt) (MID-nite)
(*n.*) 12 o'clock at night

modern (mod′ ərn) (MOD-urn)
(*adj.*) having something to do with the present time

Nn

nibble (ni′ bəl) (NI-buhl)
(*v.*) to eat with very small bites

notice (nō′ tis) (NOH-tiss)
1. (*v.*) to see something or be aware of it for the first time
2. (*n.*) a sign put up for people to read

Oo

object (äb′ jikt) (OB-jikt)
(*n.*) a thing you can see or touch

ocean (ō′ shən) (OH-shuhn)
(*n.*) a very large area of salt water that covers almost three quarters of Earth

odd (äd) (OD)
1. (*adj.*) not what you are used to
2. (*adj.*) cannot be divided evenly by two

Pp

pack (pak) (PAK)
1. (*v.*) to put things into a container, such as a bag, box, or suitcase
2. (*n.*) a group of something, such as animals, people, or things

pain (pān) (PAYN)
(*n.*) a feeling of hurt

pale (pāl) (PAYL)
(*adj.*) having little color

pass (pas) (PASS)
1. (*v.*) to go by someone or something
2. (*n.*) a piece of paper that says the holder can do something or go someplace

passenger (pas′ ən jər) (PASS-uhn-jur)
(*n.*) someone who travels in a vehicle but is not the driver

pitch (pich) (PICH)
(*v.*) to throw

plant (plant) (PLANT)
1. (*n.*) a living thing that grows in soil or in water. It often has green leaves.
2. (*v.*) to put something, such as a seed, into the ground so that it can grow

prepare (pri pâr′) (pri-PAIR)
(*v.*) to get ready

present (pre′ zənt) (PRE-zuhnt)
1. (*n.*) something that is given to someone out of kindness
2. (*adj.*) in a place at a certain time

proper (präp′ ər) (PROP-ur)
(*adj.*) right or correct

prove (prüv) (PROOV)
(*v.*) to show that something is true

Rr

rainbow (rān′ bō) (RAYN-boh)
(*n.*) long stripes of color that appear in the sky after a rainfall

relax (ri laks′) (ri-LAKS)
(*v.*) to become less tense

Ss

safe (sāf) (SAYF)
1. (*adj.*) not in danger of being harmed or stolen
2. (*n.*) a strong box in which you can lock up money and other valuable things

scatter (ska′ tər) (SKA-tur)
(*v.*) to throw things over a large area

scrape (skrāp) (SKRAPE)
1. (*v.*) to rub something against a rough or sharp surface
2. (*n.*) a mark made on a surface by rubbing or scratching against something rough or sharp

screech (skrēch) (SKREECH)
1. (*n.*) a loud, high sound
2. (*v.*) to make a loud sound

seal (sēl) (SEEL)
1. (*n.*) a sea animal that has thick fur and flippers. A seal can swim and live in cold places.
2. (*v.*) to close up tightly

search (sûrch) (SURCH)
(*v.*) to look for or try to find

GLOSSARY

seashell (sē′ shel) (SEE-shel)
(*n.*) the shell of a sea animal such as an oyster or clam

section (sek′ shən) (SEK-shuhn)
(*n.*) part of a whole

select (si lekt′) (si-LEKT)
(*v.*) to pick something out

separate
1. (*v.*) (sep′ ə rāt) (SEP-uh-rate) to sort or set apart
2. (*adj.*) (sep′ ər it) (SEP-ur-it) not joined

shiver (shi′ vər) (SHI-vur)
(*v.*) to shake quickly when cold or afraid

signal (sig′ nəl) (SIG-nuhl)
(*n.*) anything that sends a message or a warning

similar (sim′ ə lər) (SIM-uh-lur)
(*adj.*) alike; much the same

slender (slen′ dər) (SLEN-dur)
(*adj.*) thin

smooth (smüth) (SMOOTH)
(*adj.*) not rough and bumpy, but flat and even

sniff (snif) (SNIF)
(*v.*) to take in air through your nose in short, quick breaths

snowstorm (snō′ stôrm) (SNOH-storm)
(*n.*) a storm with a lot of snow

soar (sôr) (SOR)
(*v.*) to fly very high in the air

soil (soil) (SOYL)
(*n.*) the dirt or earth that plants grow in

squeeze (skwēz) (SKWEEZ)
(*v.*) to hold something tightly

stable (stā′ bəl) (STAY-buhl)
1. (*n.*) a building where horses are kept
2. (*adj.*) strong and not easily moved

stack (stak) (STAK)
1. (*n.*) a neat pile of something
2. (*v.*) to pile one thing on top of another

stamp (stamp) (STAMP)
1. (*n.*) a small piece of printed paper that shows when postage is paid
2. (*v.*) to put your foot down with force

steady (ste′ dē) (STE-dee)
(*adj.*) continuing and not changing much

steep (stēp) (STEEP)
(*adj.*) having a sharp slope; difficult to go up

steer (stēr) (STIHR)
1. (*v.*) to move something in a certain direction
2. (*n.*) a bull that is raised for meat

stream (strēm) (STREEM)
(*n.*) a body of flowing water that is narrow and shallow

Tt

task (task) (TASK)
(*n.*) a job to be done

team (tēm) (TEEM)
(*n.*) a group of people who work together or play a sport together

tender (ten' dər) (TEN-dur)
(*adj.*) soft and easy to cut

tense (tens) (TENSS)
(*adj.*) not able to relax

tiny (tī' nē) (TYE-nee)
(*adj.*) very small

tool (tül) (TOOL)
(*n.*) a piece of equipment used to do a certain job

trail (trāl) (TRAYL)
(*n.*) a path for people to follow, especially in the woods

travel (tra' vəl) (TRA-vuhl)
(*v.*) to go from one place to another

tremble (trem' bəl) (TREM-buhl)
(*v.*) to shake a little from excitement or anger

Vv

village (vi' lij) (VI-lij)
(*n.*) a small town

Ww

warn (wôrn) (WORN)
(*v.*) to tell someone about possible danger

wave (wāv) (WAYV)
1. (*v.*) to move your hand back and forth
2. (*n.*) something that looks like a long bump moving through the water in a lake or an ocean

weak (wēk) (WEEK)
(*adj.*) not strong

weekend (wēk' end) (WEEK-end)
(*n.*) the two days of the week called Saturday and Sunday

whisper (hwis' pər) (WISS-pur)
(*v.*) to speak in a very soft and quiet voice

whole (hōl) (HOLE)
(*adj.*) complete; having all its parts

wise (wīz) (WIZE)
(*adj.*) showing good sense and judgment

wonder (wən' dər) (WUHN-dur)
(*v.*) to be curious about something

worry (wər' ē) (WUR-ee)
(*v.*) to feel that something bad may happen

GLOSSARY

Word List

The words below are taught in this book. The number after each word tells you the page where you can find the word.

accept, 144
address, 144
admire, 152
agree, 60
alarm, 78
arrive, 38
attach, 152

bare, 60
beach, 30
beam, 122
bench, 16
board, 108
branch, 8
brave, 8
bridge, 16
bright, 52

calm, 100
carve, 122
center, 30
cheer, 100
chew, 52
clear, 38
collect, 78
cross, 16
crowd, 16
curious, 108

damp, 78
dangerous, 108
dash, 8
dawn, 100

deep, 16
den, 122
difficult, 144
dive, 86
doubt, 108

eager, 108
enemy, 86
enormous, 38
entire, 100
escape, 130
evening, 8
exactly, 38
excuse, 144
expert, 145

fair, 100
famous, 60
fear, 109
feast, 60
field, 101
finally, 30
float, 38
flour, 52
forest, 52
fresh, 17
frighten, 86
frown, 17

gentle, 60
greedy, 8

handle, 152
harm, 101

herd, 86
hero, 61
hollow, 145
honest, 130
hour, 52

idea, 30
inn, 53
insect, 78
island, 53

label, 130
leader, 61
lean, 122
leap, 109

major, 152
midnight, 39
modern, 130

nibble, 53
notice, 61

object, 130
ocean, 30
odd, 122

pack, 86
pain, 101
pale, 53
pass, 9
passenger, 152

pitch, 131
plant, 78
prepare, 153
present, 9
proper, 123
prove, 87

rainbow, 39
relax, 145

safe, 79
scatter, 79
scrape, 123
screech, 109
seal, 87
search, 61
seashell, 31
section, 145
select, 131
separate, 153
shiver, 101
signal, 17
similar, 153
slender, 153
smooth, 87
sniff, 131
snowstorm, 39
soar, 87
soil, 79
squeeze, 109
stable, 131
stack, 31
stamp, 145
steady, 87
steep, 131

steer, 123
stream, 9

task, 153
team, 79
tender, 123
tense, 123
tiny, 31
tool, 79
trail, 9
travel, 17
tremble, 101

village, 109

warn, 53
wave, 31
weak, 61
weekend, 39
whisper, 39
whole, 145
wise, 9
wonder, 31
worry, 17